Supersonic Fighter Development

Roy Braybrook

Foulis

Haynes

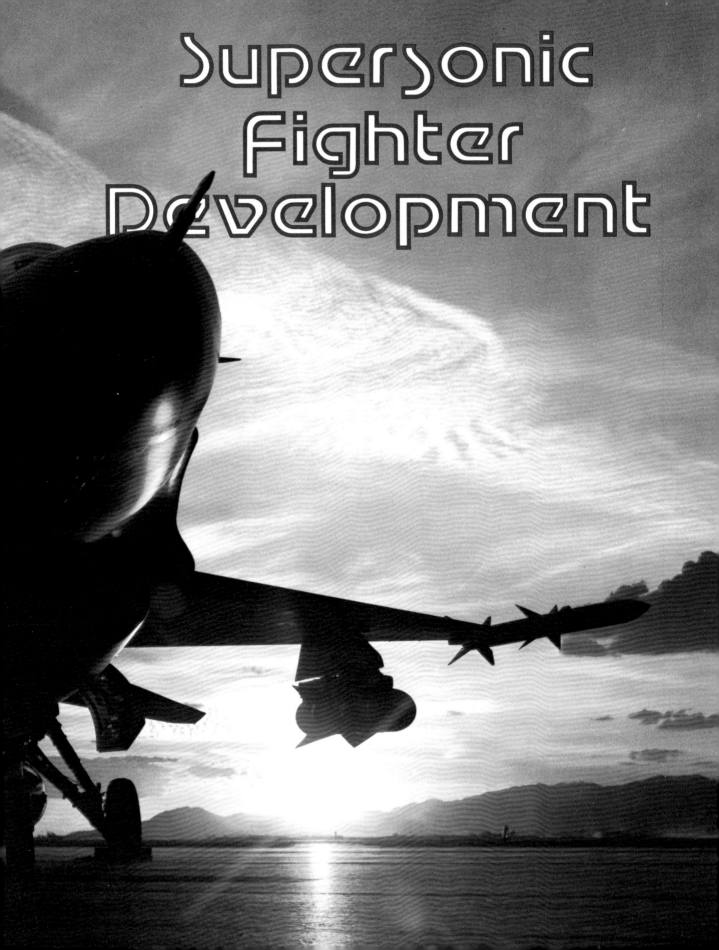

Preceding pages: A General Dynamics F-16 Fighting Falcon, with two Hughes AGM-65 Maverick air-ground missiles under the wings, and a pair of Hughes AIM-120 AMRAAM (advanced medium-range air-air missiles) on the wingtips. (General Dynamics)

ISBN 0 85429 582 8

A **FOULIS** Aviation Book

First published 1987

© Haynes Publishing Group 1987

Published by:
Haynes Publishing Group
Sparkford, Nr. Yeovil, Somerset
BA22 7JJ, England.

Haynes Publications Inc.
861 Lawrence Drive, Newbury Park,
California 91320, USA.

British Library Cataloguing in Publication data
Braybrook, Roy
  Supersonic fighter development
  1. Supersonic fighter planes
  I. Title
  623.74.'64   UG1242.F5
  ISBN 0-85429-582-8

Library of Congress catalog card number
  87-80606

Editor: Mansur Darlington
Layout design: Mike King
Printed in England by: J.H. Haynes & Co.

Contents

Introduction

THE DEVELOPMENT of combat aircraft may be regarded with some justification as the cutting-edge of aviation technology. This is the category of aircraft that wins battles, if not wars. This is the area in which technology can be pushed to the limits, knowing that the only lives at risk are those of professional military pilots.

Throughout aviation history, fighters have progressed in a series of distinct phases, stimulated by technological advances and the needs of war. Examples of early developments included the synchronizing of machine guns to fire through propellers, the advent of cantilever monoplane wings, retractable undercarriages, closed cockpits, metal monocoque airframes, aerial cannon, variable-pitch airscrews, high-compression engines burning leaded fuels, and (in WWII) relatively lightweight air-intercept (AI) radars.

The development of turbojet engines (initially in Germany and Britain) marked a watershed in fighter progress, since speeds were no longer limited by shock wave effects on the propeller tips. All the rotating parts of the engine were now contained in a duct, hence the speed of the airflow could be restricted, and the Mach number of the compressor blades could be made less than that of the aircraft itself. Instead of the thrust decaying rapidly at high subsonic Mach numbers, it now continued at a virtually constant level. The turbojet engine had opened the door to supersonic flight, although it would require airframes of reduced wave drag, and (for high Mach numbers) special types of intake that would compress the air

efficiently. Thin, swept wings allowed fighters to exceed the speed of sound in level flight, aircraft such as the F-100 Super Sabre and MiG-19 reaching speeds in the region of Mach 1.3 by the mid-1950s. Multi-shock intakes and more powerful afterburning engines then made possible speeds in excess of Mach 2, at which stage a plateau was produced by the temperature limit on aluminium alloys. Substantially higher speeds were to necessitate the use of new airframe materials, such as titanium and special steels.

Aside from opening the way to high speeds and altitudes, the gas turbine engine changed fighter development in other ways. The need for aerodynamically slender airframes brought a fresh significance to the technical sections of design offices. Flying controls required power-assistance, and later fully-powered operation. Cockpits had to be pressurized and fitted with ejection seats, to provide safe escapes under difficult conditions. The growing complexity of aircraft systems led to larger design teams, with a higher percentage of college graduates.

As technical problems multiplied and design staffs grew to deal with them, fighter development became even more of a team effort, involving much longer gestation periods and far more expenditure. Just after WWII it was possible for a fighter to go from preliminary design to first flight in less than three years, and enter service after a further similar period. The Hawker Hunter was conceived in 1948, flew in 1951, and entered service in 1954 despite major technical problems. Nowadays a period of ten years from conception to initial operational capability (IOC) is regarded as

Technologically the most advanced fighter of WWII, the Messerschmitt Me 262 combined slightly swept wings with Jumo 004 axial-flow engines and an armament of four 30 mm MK108 cannon. This Me 262A-1 (Wk Nr 112372) flew with JG7 late in the war. (Roy Braybrook)

normal, the Eurofighter EFA planned in 1985 being aimed at service in 1995.

The advent of the jet engine thus marked a new era in fighter progress in many respects, and this book is accordingly restricted to a discussion of jet-powered combat aircraft. To keep the size of the book within reason, its scope is further limited to fighters as they exist today and are likely to exist in the next few decades. It thus omits detailed discussion of the first (subsonic) jet generation.

For convenience, this story of supersonic fighter development is broken down into three main sections. The first deals with what may be regarded as obsolescent aircraft, such as the early Mirage series, ie, the first Mach 2 fighter generation, which made its début around 1960.

The first postwar swept-wing fighters represented a consolidation of the airframe work done in Germany during the war. Typical of the period was this Hawker Hunter, which was transonic in a dive. (British Aerospace)

Sparked off by the Korean War of 1950-53 and by the threat of the nuclear-armed bomber, this generation featured all kinds of wing planforms, from the delta of the Mirage III and the highly swept wing of the Lightning and Su-7 to the tiny, razor-thin straight wing of the F-104 Starfighter.

There followed a period of consolidation, in which turbojets were superseded by more economical turbofan engines (which also gave massive afterburning boosts in thrust), and in which variable-sweep wings were introduced to give STOL performance, protracted subsonic endurance, and a smoother ride during high-speed penetrations. Saab-Scania rejected the swing-wing concept as too complex and risky, adopting instead a canard arrangement for its remarkable Viggen STOL multi-role combat aircraft series.

In the same way that the Korean War encouraged the development of the first Mach 2 generation, the Vietnam War of 1965-75 encouraged work on a new generation of fighters that would provide a major advance in air

Dassault-Breguet's Mach 2 delta-wing Mirage has been one of the outstanding successes of postwar European aviation. This example is a Brazilian Air Force Mirage IIIEBR. (AMD-BA)

The Lockheed F-104 Starfighter represented a totally different approach to Mach 2 design, using a small unswept wing of extreme slenderness. (Lockheed Corp)

The BAC Lightning (seen here in F3 form) was another different approach, using a very high sweep angle that made possible a thicker section, capable of housing the main undercarriage. The wingtips are sawn off to place the ailerons on the torsional axis. (Roy Braybrook)

combat performance. In the case of the US, this improvement was to be applicable to quite long ranges, since there was pressure to reduce the fighter's need for tanker support. This new air combat generation is instanced by the American 'Teen-Series' fighters and by the Dassault-Breguet Mirage 2000. It was made possible by engines of high thrust/weight ratio, new aerodynamic concepts such as leading edge extensions (LEXs) and automatic manoeuvre flaps, and by black-box stability and fly-by-wire (FBW) controls.

The third part of the book discusses fighters that (at time of writing) are still at a relatively early stage of their development, as exemplified by the Lavi, JAS 39, Rafale and Eurofighter EFA. It is a matter of semantics, whether such aircraft represent a completely new generation, or a consolidation of the air combat fighters that made their débuts in the 1970s. In this case the new family of aircraft was inspired, not by a war, but by the fear that the latest Soviet fighters (ie, the MiG-29 and Su-27) had overtaken the West, and by the knowledge that major technological advances were

The Saab-Scania Viggen adopted a canard layout for short take-off and landing from dispersed road sites. This JA37 interceptor is shown armed with two BAe Sky Flash air-air missiles and a belly-mounted Oerlikon KCA 30 mm cannon. (A. Anderson, Saab-Scania)

The General Dynamics F-16 Fighting Falcon represented a major step forward, with high thrust/weight ratio, an advanced cockpit, relaxed static stability and fly-by-wire controls. (General Dynamics)

The Dassault-Breguet Mirage 2000 combines the low wave drag of the delta wing with the advantages of natural longitudinal instability, giving reduced trim drag and higher lift coefficients. Note the leading edge flaps. (AMD-BA)

available in the fields of powerplants, airframe configurations, and operational equipment. One of the main innovations now available is the design of combat aircraft for 'stealth' characteristics, although little hard information is available on this topic. Nonetheless, this book attempts to make some predictions as to how fighters will develop in the forseeable future.

One of the fundamental problems in any discussion of aircraft is that many of the terms in general use have never been strictly defined. With that in mind, it may be desirable for the writer to clarify at least his own use of terms relating to the principal fighter roles. In general, the term *'fighter'* is used to denote an aircraft that is designed primarily for aerial combat, which may take two main forms. Combat with other fighters is aimed at

Laying the foundations for the Eurofighter EFA, the British Aerospace EAP features a cranked-delta wing, a foreplane mounted to give an outstanding rear view, a high composite content, and a low-drag missile installation. (British Aerospace).

gaining some degree of control of the airspace, hence one refers to *air superiority* fighters, *air combat* fighters, or simply dogfight aircraft. The destruction of intruding bombers and reconnaissance aircraft implies a somewhat different aircraft, with emphasis on top-end performance (high Mach, high altitude), as in the case of the MiG-31. Such aircraft are referred to as *air defence* fighters or interceptors.

Probably the nicest-looking of the new fighters, the Dassault-Breguet Rafale-A is quite different from the EAP in terms of canard location and foreplane position. (AMD-BA)

On current plans, there will be at least 800 Eurofighter EFAs built by Britain, Germany, Italy and Spain, and the aircraft will enter service in 1995. (Eurofighter/Jagdflugzeug GmbH)

However, there is also a case for introducing the term *strike* fighter to cover such aircraft as the Tornado IDS, since (although designed for the air-ground role) it has a sufficiently high performance to be adaptable in principle to air defence. An even better example is the AJ37 Viggen, which is primarily used for ground attack, but has a secondary interception capability.

Aviation terminology is a transient thing, as illustrated by the 'fighting scouts' of WWI and the 'fighter-bombers' of WWII and Korea. In considering the history of combat aircraft, however, what matters is not the terms used, but why fighters have changed in terms of their external shape, their powerplants and operational equipment. This book attempts to put such matters into perspective.

Roy Braybrook

Chapter 1

The Obsolescent Generation

AT PRESENT the fighters in front-line service with the principal air forces may be regarded as belonging to two categories: obsolescent aircraft such as the Mirage III and F-4 Phantom II, which are subjects of this first chapter, and replacements such as the Mirage 2000 and America's 'Teen-Series' aircraft, which will be discussed later. This simple division of aircraft types is in general an accurate perception of the combat aircraft situation, although it can be argued that some fighters (including the F-14, Viggen and Tornado) either fall somewhere between the two generations or bridge the gap between them.

The term 'obsolescent' is perhaps somewhat unkind, since only outstanding fighters from the 1950s and 60s still survive with the major operators, and since with modern operational equipment these aircraft remain very effective. For example, a German Air Force F-4F updated with Hughes APG-65 radar (as developed for the F/A-18) and an armament of four AMRAAM and four ASRAAM will be an extremely serious aeroplane.

Despite such reservations, it is convenient in a historical discussion of this nature to regard a large number of different aircraft types as representatives of a single generation, and to designate one such generation as obsolescent on the grounds that replacements are under active development, if not actually in service.

The nature of any fighter generation is the end-product of a number of factors, including the past experience of the manufacturers and operators

The Dassault-Breguet Mirage III/5 series (represented here by an M5 in old Libyan Air Force markings) took over the export market from the Hawker Hunter. The Mirage offers Mach 2 capability with optional rocket boost for high altitude intercepts, and a useful high-speed strike performance. (AMD-BA)

Germany's updated F-4F with Hughes APG-65 radar and four semi-recessed AMRAAMs is illustrated by this artist's impression. (MMB)

involved, the emerging technologies of the period, and the wars and other major events that may have shaped thinking by air staffs and designers.

Previous experience certainly plays a part in determining the principal role for a fighter. Traditionally, European and Soviet designers have produced fast-climbing interceptors with a high altitude ceiling. Such aircraft are also good in dogfights, due to their low wing loadings and high thrust/weight ratios, but are limited to short ranges by their low fuel fractions. In contrast, American designers have traditionally excelled at long-range escort fighters, much larger aircraft with significantly higher fuel fractions than their European contemporaries, but with poor rates of climb and lower ceilings.

Going back to WWII, this contrast in primary roles was to be seen in the differences between Britain's Spitfire and America's P-51 Mustang, P-47 Thunderbolt, and P-38 Lightning. It was a fundamental difference that was to continue into the jet era, since European nations were concerned with wars on their own borders and with defending cities that might be attacked with very little warning, whereas America's cities were relatively safe, and priority could be given to strategic bombing across vast stretches of ocean.

The most important event affecting fighters that began their development between the mid-1940s and mid-1960s was the dropping of the first US atomic bombs, on Hiroshima on 6 August 1945 and on Nagasaki

European designers have traditionally excelled at fast-climbing interceptors that are also good in dogfights. One of the greatest was the Vickers-Supermarine Spitfire, exemplified by this Mk IX, MH434. (Roy Braybrook)

three days later. This undoubtedly encouraged the Russians to redouble their efforts to produce fast-climbing interceptors. Relations between East and West deteriorated during the course of 1946, and, on the widely-held assumption that the Soviet Union would have its own atomic bombs in the course of the 1950s, European manufacturers set out to produce the best possible air defence fighters. The first such aircraft with swept wings (if one ignores German WWII fighters) was the Saab J29 'Flying Barrel', which had its maiden flight on 1 September 1948. Only in 1951 was it joined by the original Dassault Mystère, on 23 February, and the Hawker Hunter, on 20 July.

The first Soviet atomic device was actually detonated on 19 September 1949, somewhat ahead of Western predictions. However, content in the knowledge that the Russians lacked the means to make effective bombing attacks against US population centres, and that any such missions (presumably flight-refuelled, one-way sorties) could be intercepted out over Canada, America continued to produce machine gun armed,

America produced some outstanding long-range fighters in WWII, such as this Republic P-47 Thunderbolt, now on show at the Musée de l'Air at Le Bourget. (Roy Braybrook)

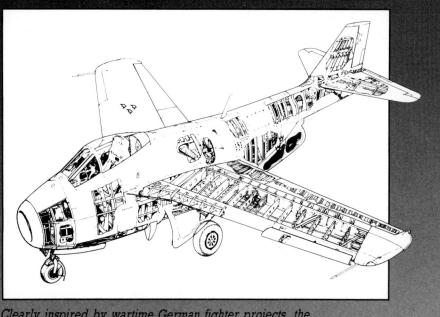

Clearly inspired by wartime German fighter projects, the Saab J29 was Europe's first postwar swept-wing fighter. Note the leading edge slats. (Saab-Scania)

What is presumably a photograph of Swedish Air Force J29s toward the end of their service, this shows the aircraft in both side- and plan-view. The Sidewinders and fixed leading-edge extensions are noteworthy (Saab Scania)

The greatest of Europe's early postwar swept-wing fighters was the Hawker Hunter, which was designed as a high altitude interceptor, but achieved distinction in the ground attack role. (British Aerospace)

relatively slow-climbing air superiority fighters. The **F-86 Sabre,** which first flew on 1 October 1947, was in this sense a true descendant of the P-51 of WWII.

The F-86 was one of the greatest fighters of all time, along with the Spitfire and Me 109. Not only did it prove a quantum leap in maximum speed through the use of the latest technology (a swept wing and an axial-flow engine), but it also fought in a war of significant duration and achieved an outstanding kill-ratio against what was then the latest Communist equipment.

The Korean War lasted from June 1950 to July 1953. Deliveries of the F-86 to the first USAF operational unit had begun only in February 1949, so it was still a relatively new and untested aircraft that went to Korea in the following year, to replace the straight-wing F-80C Shooting Star in the air superiority role. Russia's swept-wing MiG-15 (Fagot), which had first flown in July 1947, made its appearance in Korea on 1 November 1950, posing a

These four Sabres (serials 47-631, -626, -627 and -632) were taken from the first production batch of F-86A-1s, deliveries of which began in 1948, although the first operational squadron was not to receive Sabres until February 1949. (Rockwell International Corp)

serious threat to USAF operations. Seven days later the first F-86 wing was ordered to prepare to move to Korea, and the first F-86 combat missions were flown on 17 December.

As its name implies, most air combats took place in 'MiG Alley', an area in the north-west of Korea, just below the Yalu River that forms the border with China. At the time it was believed that most of the MiG-15s were flown by Chinese pilots, but subsequent information indicated that they were mainly Soviet squadrons, rotated at six-week intervals, although

The only jet fighter used by the USAF in the early part of the Korean War was the Lockheed F-80 Shooting Star, represented here by a P-80A. Around 270 were deployed, dropping over 40,000 tons of bombs and napalm, firing more than 80,000 rockets, and destroying six MiGs for the loss of 14 F-80s in air-air combat. (Lockheed Corp)

some Chinese and Polish units were also involved. The Communist aircraft operated from bases around Antung just beyond the Yalu, where they were safe from attack.

From USAF bases around Seoul, MiG Alley represented a sortie of around 200 nm (370 km) radius, and the F-86s flew 25-minute high altitude patrols in that area. They generally flew in sections of four aircraft, up to eight sections together, and between 35,000 and 45,000 ft (10,700 – 13,700 m), depending on model. The MiG-15s crossed the border at around 50,000 ft (15.250 m), in 'trains' of 60 to 80 aircraft.

The **MiG-15bis** was superior in performance to all models of Sabre aside from the F-86F-30 (which had an extended leading edge) above 36,000 ft (11,000 m), but had inferior dive characteristics, was prone to spins, lacked radar ranging, had a difficult mixture of 23 and 37 mm cannon, and was generally flown by inexperienced pilots. The point is also worth making that, although the MiGs could choose when to join combat with the Sabres, the altitude was set by the Sabres' cruise height.

According to USAF sources, the F-86 destroyed 792 MiG-15s (aside from 118 'probables' and 808 damaged) for the loss of 78 aircraft in air-air combat, giving a kill-ratio of almost exactly 10:1. Although a great deal was made at the time of the value of radar ranging as a means automatically to correct the ballistic drop of the F-86's 0.50-inch (12.7 mm) machine guns, it is now admitted that almost all the Sabre's kills were made without benefit of radar. Most pilots in Korea in fact got their kills using a fixed gunsight setting and from the 6 o'clock position, just as pilots did in WWI and WWII.

It is estimated that the Communist effort peaked at around 1,800 aircraft, including 950 MiGs (over 400 were parked on one airfield!). By the end of the war, the USAF had seven fighter wings in Korea, with 297 F-86s and 218 F-84s, although 132 F-86s and all the F-84s were allocated to ground attack missions. Sabre operations peaked at a remarkable 7,696

The MiG-15 provided a nasty shock for the Allies when it appeared in Korea. Shown here are two MiG-15bis, representing the air forces of Czechoslovakia (foreground) and Poland (rear). (US Department of Defense)

sorties in June 1953, corresponding to approximately 26 sorties per aircraft for that month.

Korea in Perspective

The Korean War has been discussed in some detail because it had a profound effect on Western thinking. The unheralded advent of the MiG-15 came as a surprise in several respects. It showed that the Soviet Union had continued its fighter development effort at a wartime level, combining the fruits of German swept-wing research and British developments on centrifugal-flow turbojet engines. From an American viewpoint the MiG-15 represented a remarkable achievement in terms of performance, although its systems were crude in comparison with those of the F-86.

It could be argued that a 10:1 kill ratio in favour of the F-86 was proof of a massive American superiority, but this would be an oversimplification. Probably the most significant factor on the US side was the experience and training of USAF pilots. A typical F-86 pilot was vastly superior to a typical MiG-15 pilot, but the USAF had nonetheless been forced to deploy its latest and best equipment in order to achieve satisfactory results. Nor can it have been lost on staff officers in the Pentagon that all the combats had taken place at altitudes chosen to suit the performance of the F-86.

The correct perception of air combat in Korea was that the actual results had been good, but that in somewhat different circumstances the balance could easily have gone against the USAF. When allowances were made for the peaks and troughs in effectiveness produced by aircraft replacement cycles, and the fact that an aggressor can choose his time to attack on the basis of exploiting his own equipment peaks and the defender's troughs, it was evident from the Korean experience that there would be occasions when the Russians could win in the air.

One of the foundation-stones of US fighter development is the fact that American forces have increasingly taken air supremacy for granted. There were certainly times during WWII when American ground forces were subjected to enemy air attacks, but in the later years such occasions were the exceptions rather than the rule. In Korea, air attacks on US positions were practically unknown. The only bombs dropped on USAF airfields were delivered by an old biplane, known as 'Bedcheck Charlie'. One might add (leaping ahead chronologically) that a similar situation applied in Vietnam, but without the biplane.

Over the years, and certainly since the Korean War, American control of the air over the country's own forces has become the norm. However, once air supremacy is taken for granted in operational planning, suspicions arise (externally and internally) that American ground forces cannot win in a tactical environment involving air inferiority. There are thus enormous pressures on the USAF to maintain air superiority, and a large slice of the service's budget is directed toward fulfilling this specific objective.

The Korean War had the effect of stimulating within the US a major effort to establish a worthwhile lead over the Soviets in terms of air combat

fighters. The MiG-15 had demonstrated that a reasonably high performance could be achieved with relatively crude technology. Given afterburning axial-flow engines and thinner, more highly swept wings, subsequent MiGs threatened to achieve much higher speeds and completely outclass the F-86 and the early 'Century-Series'. The need was therefore for a fighter in the Mach 2 category, which would outclass forseeable Russian developments in the sort of air combats that had taken place over Korea.

For Western Europe, both the MiG-15 and the F-86 were inspirational aircraft, demonstrating that certain countries (notably Britain and France) had been over-cautious in their attitude to German wartime research into the aerodynamic characteristics of swept wings. These countries were now encouraged in the use of such wings (despite their known tendency to tip-stall and pitch-up), although the emphasis remained on point-defence interceptors, rather than attempting to follow the US in the development of long-range escorts. Europe also aimed for higher thrust/weight ratios, and adopted 30 mm cannon that could blow a bomber apart in seconds.

This characteristic difference in design philosophy may be illustrated by comparing the **Hunter F1** with the F-86A. The British aircraft was armed

One of the main reasons for America's lead in the air was that nation's willingness to spend money and risk lives in high-speed research programmes. The Bell X-1 rocket-powered aircraft, flown by Capt (later Gen) Charles E. Yeager, USAF, exceeded Mach 1.0 in level flight on 14 October 1947. The X-1 also proved the need for a fully-powered horizontal tail. (Bell Helicopter Textron)

with four 30 mm cannon and had an internal fuel capacity of 334 imp gal (1520 litres), and a normal take-off weight of 16,200 lb (7347 kg), giving a fuel fraction of approximately 16 per cent. In contrast, the F-86A-5 was armed with six 12.7 mm machine guns, contained 362.5 imp gal (1648 litres) and had a clean weight of 14,108 lb (6400 kg), corresponding to a fuel fraction of 20 per cent. The difference in design emphasis is also shown by their thrust/weight ratio (T/W) figures. Powered by a 7500 lb (3400 kg) Avon Mk113, the Hunter F1 had a T/W of 0.463, while the F-86A-5 with a 5200 lb (2358 kg) J47-GE-13 had a T/W of only 0.369. This difference certainly showed up in climb rate, but in sustained turn performance the comparison was complicated by the fact that the F-86 had a much higher aspect ratio wing (4.79, compared to 3.33), being designed for longer ranges at high altitude.

Although this rough comparison is legitimate in illustrating the fundamentally different approaches of European and US designers, it may be noted that in other respects it falls into the old trap of 'comparing today's Hunter with yesterday's Sabre'. This happened quite often in the 1950s, even with USAF evaluation teams. In fact, the F-86A-5 entered service in 1949 and the Hunter F1 in 1954.

Before leaving the subject of the Sabre, it is also worth noting that, notwithstanding the high fuel consumption of the jet engine, it was not a vastly heavier aircraft than the piston-engined P-51 that had preceded it on the North American line. The P-51D had an empty equipped weight of 7125 lb (3232 kg) and a maximum take-off weight of 12,100 lb (5488 kg), while the F-86A-5 had an empty equipped weight of 10.093 lb (4577 kg) and a maximum weight of 16,233 lb (7362 kg) with two 1000 lb (454 kg) bombs.

Supersonics

The fact that the F-86 was a comparatively small, lightweight fighter by jet standards was significant in another sense, because it highlighted the sharp upward trend in America's succeeding 'Century-series' aircraft. By the 1950s the US had established a world lead in combat aircraft design, and European manufacturers had come to regard the products of their American counterparts as indicative of where the whole industry was heading. It was logical enough that jet fighters would be heavier than their piston-engined predecessors, since (for the first time) pilots could actually see the needle on the fuel gauge moving! It also seemed sensible that the introduction of afterburners would again lead to a substantial jump in aircraft weights, as (for a given thrust) the fuel flow rate was more than doubled. Since America was now ahead in fighter development, it was US aircraft that European designers looked at for guidance on realistic sizes.

In this writer's view, the upward trend in US Century-Series fighters was somewhat misleading, since these aircraft were designed for longer ranges than Europe required, and since their development had begun before the Korean War, which had emphasized the value of using large numbers of relatively small aircraft. This US trend certainly encouraged Hawker Aircraft, then the principal UK fighter team, to embark on a series of comparatively heavy projects that would have been expensive to develop and far too costly for the export market. The end result was that Hawker, having sold the subsonic Hunter in most regions of the world, then lost the export market to Dassault, who produced in the Mirage III an affordable multi-role fighter, exactly what the market was looking for.

The first of the Century-Series was the **North American F-100 Super Sabre,** which was also the first US fighter to be capable of supersonic speeds in level flight. Whereas aircraft such as the Hunter and F-86 had required steep dives from high altitude to exceed Mach 1.0, the F-100 could reach speeds up to Mach 1.3 on the level, though only over a narrow band of altitudes around 36,000 ft (11,000 m). One consequence was that speed records were from this point onward set at altitude rather than at sea level, the F-100C achieving a figure of 822 mph (1323 km/hr).

The YF-100A had its maiden flight on 25 May 1953, and operational capability was achieved in September 1954, only two months after Britain's RAF received its first subsonic Hunters. In level flight performance terms the Soviet equivalent of the F-100 is the MiG-19 (Farmer), which flew without afterburners in late 1952 and became operational (after some accidents) in 1955.

The F-100 is a much larger aircraft than the F-86, with 45 degrees of quarter-chord sweep, compared to 35 degrees on the Sabre. Wing thickness/chord ratio (t/c) was reduced from the Sabre's 9 to 7 per cent. Like the original F-86 (and most subsequent models), the F-100 retains automatic leading edge slats. At high lift coefficients these slats move forwards on guides under the action of leading edge suction. They delay

First of the Century-Series fighters, the North American
F-100A Super Sabre could reach around Mach 1.3 in level flight over a narrow altitude band. Note the tall fin and low-set tail. (Rockwell International Corp)

Although it never equalled the success of the F-86, the F-100 (seen here in F-100D form) was a well-built aeroplane with a great deal of internal fuel, allowing it to perform a useful ground attack mission and defend itself against enemy fighters. (Rockwell International Corp)

Hawker Aircraft believed the trend was toward high weights and projected a series of heavy fighters such as the P.1121, shown here in mock-up form. (British Aerospace)

stalling by creating a sheet of high velocity air over the upper surface of the wings.

One of the basic tendencies of swept wings is to stall at the tips, producing pitch-up. This tendency to longitudinal instability is worsened if the tailplane (or horizontal stabilizer) is placed higher than the wing, with the result that the downwash gradient at the tail is increasing just as the wingtips begin to stall. The effect of this is that the tailplane contribution to stability is reduced and the aerodynamic centre moves forwards, decreasing longitudinal stability.

In terms of design for good longitudinal stability, the F-100 was an improvement on the F-86, since its tailplane was set low on the fuselage. It may be noted that the MiG-19 also featured a tailplane moved in the right direction. The setting of the tail of the preceding MiG-15 and -17, however, had been high on the fin (or vertical stabilizer), and that of the MiG-19 was moved only as far as the upper fuselage.

Aside from emphasizing the trend to higher weights, the F-100 illustrated a trend to fuselages that were long and heavy in comparison to the size of the wing. The length of the fuselage was partly associated with achieving a high fineness ratio in order to reduce wave drag, but it also reflected the increasing complexity of aircraft, and the fact that most of the equipment was carried in the fuselage. Meanwhile, wings were gradually becoming thinner (which was pushing more of the fuel into the fuselage) and smaller, in order to increase maximum speed.

This concentration of weight in a long fuselage was no great problem if the aircraft rolled about its true longitudinal axis. However, in a rolling pull-out manoeuvre the aircraft would be flying at a considerable angle of attack (AOA). The result was then a pitching moment due to the centrifugal forces on the various weights in the front and rear fuselage. With the aircraft acting like a gyroscope, the pitching moment could create a sideslip (due to precession), possibly even tearing the fin off.

The mathematical equations for 'inertial cross-coupling' are quite complicated, but certain aspects of the problem may be discussed in simple terms. For example, the difference between the aircraft's inertias in pitch and roll must be limited if cross-coupling difficulties are to be avoided. This consideration in fact halted the trend toward extremely long aircraft with tiny wings, such as the **Douglas X-3.**

Although the rolling pull-out case is probably the critical one, divergence in yaw can also occur in a straight roll. The two standard 'fixes' are to increase fin area and to limit roll rate. In the case of the F-100C, the vertical tail area was increased first by 27 per cent, and later by a further 14 per cent. To complete discussion of this aspect of development, the F-102 and -106 had fin increases of over 30 per cent (and the latter a stiffened fuselage), the F-104 had a ventral fin added, and the F-105 had a 60 per cent increase in fin area, and additional fin stiffness. The F-105 was also given a boost in directional stability in the form of a yaw damper that came into operation at a rate of roll of 50 deg/sec.

As mentioned earlier, one way to attack the inertia roll-coupling

In the 1950s the trend appeared to be toward heavy fighters with long fuselages and extremely high wing loadings. The Douglas X-3 exemplified the trend. It was test-flown between 1952 and 1956. (McDonnell Douglas Corp)

problem was to restrict aileron travel, and thus limit roll rate. In the case of the F-101, this was reportedly achieved by means of hydraulic actuator stall, which came in progressively with airspeed. For the F-102, above 400 knots (740 km/hr) IAS a large aileron breakout force was introduced at 5-degree surface deflection. In the case of the F-106, stops were set at 6.3 degrees aileron deflection. For the F-104, aileron travel was reduced by

The X-3 or 'Flying Stiletto' used titanium and stainless steel in its tiny, thin wings, and (unlike the X-1) had a single-piece ('slab') horizontal tail. (McDonnell Douglas Corp)

two-thirds, and with the later F-104G stops were set at 7 degrees with flaps up, and 20 degrees with flaps down. In addition, all these aircraft have some form of autostabilization, and flight limitations in the event that one or more channels becomes inoperative. Even with the autostabilizer fully operational, there is usually a restriction on rolls in excess of 180/360 degrees beyond certain g-values.

Because it was only marginally supersonic , the F-100 was soon replaced in the air-air role, but it continued to be employed by the USAF in the air-ground role for many years. It was also popular with America's allies as a good, solid aeroplane with a useful internal fuel capacity and an effective bombload. The F-100C was given six external hardpoints, and the F-100D was able to carry up to 7500 lb (3400 kg) externally. One indication of the sheer size of the aircraft is that it is able to carry a store on the inboard wing pylon, ahead of the main undercarriage. Such an arrangement would have been impossible in the case of an aircraft such as the Hunter or Sabre.

The **F-100D** has an empty weight of 20,638 lb, ie, twice as much as the F-86A, and an internal fuel capacity of 990 imp gal (4500 litres), representing around 27 per cent of clean gross weight. Maximum take-off weight is 38,048 lb (17,258 kg). Power is provided by a single Pratt & Whitney J57-P-21A turbo jet, giving a dry thrust of 10,200 lb (7258 kg) and 16,000 lb (7258 kg) with afterburning. A total of 2192 F-100s were built.

Although the first supersonic USAF fighter, the F-100 was not the first to have an afterburner. The radar-equipped **F-86D** with a 7500 lb (3400 kg) afterburning J47-GE-17 entered service in 1951, armed with a retractable pack of 24 'Mighty Mouse' 2.75-inch (70 mm) rockets. The F-100 was armed with four 20 mm M-39 cannon, which were tested on the F-86E/F in Korea and fitted to most F-86Hs. The US Navy FJ-2 Fury derivative of the F-86 had four 20 mm M-24 cannon, and was slightly ahead of the F-100 into service. Italy's F-86K reportedly also had four M-24s.

The F-86 and F-100 appear to have been designed as air superiority fighters, exploiting the latest available wing and powerplant technology, but neither had the combination of range and performance to excel in the role of a fighter escort. It it interesting to note that the F-86C was to have been a long-range escort derivative of the Sabre. This, however, was a very different aircraft, with an 8000 lb (3630 kg) afterburning J48-P-1 fed by lateral intakes, an empty weight increased to 14,035 lb (6365 kg), and 1318 imp gal (5990 litres) of internal fuel, representing about 41 per cent of clean gross weight. Maximum weight was 26,516 lb (12,025 kg). The project began as the NA-157 in late 1947, duly becoming the F-86C and finally the YF-93A. An order for 118 was placed in June 1948, and the first YF-93A flew on 25 January 1950. However, procurement was cancelled in order to make more funds available for bombers.

In 1952 there was a change of heart regarding long-range escort fighters, and a pre-series batch of 29 **McDonnell F-101A Voodoos** was ordered, based on the company's XF-88. The first aircraft had its maiden flight on 29 September 1954. Once again, SAC cancelled its requirement, but on this occasion the aircraft was modified to suit TAC's low level strike fighter needs. The resulting F-101C was given a stronger wing and nuclear weapon provisions. Photo-reconnaissance versions were developed (RF-101A and -101C), and the F-101B was produced as a long-range interceptor for Aerospace Defense Command (ADC). A two-seater equipped with two J57-P-13 engines, the F-101B could be armed with three

A 'vic' of Voodoos, led by a two-seat F-101B, with an F-101A on the left and an RF-101A on the right. (McDonnell Douglas Corp).

The McDonnell Voodoo is represented here by an RF-101C reconnaissance aircraft, which had four cameras in a lengthened nose and two further aft. (McDonnell Douglas Corp)

Hughes Falcon air-air missiles in addition to two nuclear-tipped unguided Douglas Genie rockets. After being phased out by ADC, 66 of these aircraft were passed to the Canadian Armed Forces (CAF).

Continuing the weight trend, the F-101C had a maximum take-off weight of 47,000 lb (21,315 kg), giving a wing loading of 128 lb/ft² (623 kg/m²). The wing t/c of the F-101

tapered from 7 per cent at the root to 6 per cent at the tip, and a maximum speed of approximately Mach 1.7 was attained at altitude.

Area Rule

The first serious US response to the threat of the Soviet nuclear bomber was the development of the **F-102 Delta Dagger** by Convair, a division of General Dynamics that prior to 1954 was a separate entity, known as the Consolidated Vultee Aircraft Corporation.

      The F-102 was noteworthy in several respects. It was the world's first supersonic delta-wing fighter. It was one of the first designs to make use of the new American concept of Area Rule. It was also the first USAF fighter to dispense with gun armament, using instead a number of guided weapons and rocket projectiles, all of which were carried internally.

The Convair F-102 Delta Dagger was the world's first supersonic delta-wing fighter and one of the first aircraft to exploit Area Rule waisting of the fuselage. (General Dynamics)

The concept of the tail-less delta-wing fighter is generally associated with Dassault-Breguet and the Mirage III/5 series, but Convair may well claim to have been the real pioneer in this field. Engineers from the San Diego plant formed part of a US aviation industry team that visited Germany shortly after VE-Day, gathering information on research activities. The team appears to have been particularly impressed with the results of wind-tunnel tests on models of delta-wing configuration, a planform that had been advocated by Dr Alexander Lippisch. Further studies of delta-wing projects were undertaken on returning to America.

The first aircraft to result from this work was the **XF-92A,** which flew in September 1948, and is believed to have been the world's first jet-powered delta. Equipped with a non-afterburning Allison J33, it reached only Mach 0.95, but it demonstrated that a tail-less delta could be given acceptable handling characteristics, and it thus encouraged the company to employ this type of planform in designing a supersonic fighter.

It may be useful to explain at this point that, in reducing wave drag to the point that 'the sound barrier' could be pierced, it was comparatively easy to design a slender fuselage, and the tail surfaces were relatively small, hence the main stumbling-block was the wave drag of the wings. This could be reduced by increasing sweep angle and using a low thickness/chord ratio (t/c), but sweepback in those days implied pitch-up, and low t/c implied new and expensive methods of construction, such as machining the skins out of solid billets of aluminium alloys.

The delta wing appeared to have possibilities, since it generated a vortex flow over its upper surface, eliminating the pitch-up. In addition, since the inboard wing (where the bending moment was greatest) had very long chord dimensions, a comparatively thick section could be used, which in turn made possible conventional methods of construction. The delta also had the advantage that it provided much more internal volume for the fuel and undercarriage.

Unfortunately, the delta wing tended to be so large that it left nowhere for the designer to locate the tailplane, or so it was often argued. With no tailplane, there was no means to trim wing-flaps, hence maximum lift coefficient was restricted, and a large wing was required to achieve an acceptable landing performance.

In any event, in January 1949 the USAF circulated a draft requirement for an all-weather interceptor to enter service in 1954, replacing the **F-86D,** the **Northrop F-89 Scorpion** and the **Lockheed F-94 Starfire.** The formal RFP was issued in June 1950, and in September 1951 the Convair design was chosen for full-scale development. The first prototype had its maiden flight on 24 October 1953, and very quickly showed the NASA's reservations about its supersonic capability (as voiced in the previous year) were well-founded. According to its designers, the F-102 would reach a speed of Mach 1.88, although NASA tunnel tests indicated far more wave drag than Convair had assumed. In the event, it was found to be incapable of supersonic flight, and a major drag reduction programme had to be undertaken.

Probably the world's first jet-powered delta-wing aircraft, the Convair XF-92A paved the way for the F-102. (General Dynamics)

Luckily for Convair, salvation was at hand, since Richard T. Whitcomb of NASA had invented what became known as Area Rule. In its simplest form (ie, in optimizing the aircraft shape for transonic acceleration) Area Rule said that wave drag at Mach 1.0 could be minimized by ensuring that the longitudinal distribution of cross-section area followed a smooth curve (the mathematical optimum being a Sears-Haack shape). In practice, this meant that the F-102 fuselage had to be waisted in line with the wing, and the rapid decrease in cross-section at the rear had to be moderated by adding 'Whitcomb bodies' – fairings that were also applied to the wing of the Convair 990 airliner.

This Northrop F-89A Scorpion was powered by two afterburning Allison J35 turbojets, and was armed with six 20 mm cannon in the nose and (on this occasion) 16 5-inch (127 mm) HVARs under the wings. (Northrop Corp)

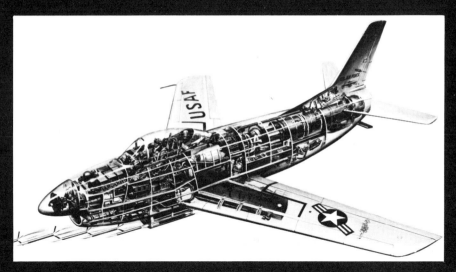

The North American F-86D Sabre 'Dog' had a nose radar, an afterburning General Electric J47 engine, and a retractable pack of 24 2.75-inch (70 mm) Mighty Mouse unguided air-air rockets. (Rockwell International Corp)

Flight-test line-up of F-89Ds with massive wingtip pods, each containing 250 imp gal (1136 litres) of fuel and 52 2.75 inch (70 mm) rockets. In this model the nose housed a new Hughes fire control system, and the six cannon were deleted. (Northrop Corp) 1/24

With these and other modifications, the first YF-102A took to the air in December 1954, and achieved a level speed of Mach 1.22. As indicated earlier, the F-102 received an enlarged fin in early 1956, and finally entered service with ADC around the middle of the year. The wing t/c was 4.0 per cent.

The F-102A was powered by a 17,200 lb (7800 kg) J57-P-23A, and had a maximum take-off weight of 32,000 lb (14,500 kg). Internal fuel was 904 imp gal (4100 litres), corresponding to around 25 per cent of clean gross weight. The F-102 was followed on the Convair line by the largely redesigned **F-106 Delta Dart,** which first flew on 26 December 1956 and

was powered by a 24,500 lb (11,100 kg) J75-P-17. It achieved a speed of Mach 2.31, compared to the Mach 1.25 of the production F-102. It had a maximum take off weight of 38,250 lb (17,350 kg).

The F-102 was armed with 24 2.75-inch (70 mm) unguided rockets and up to six AIM-4 Falcon guided weapons, which used either radar- or IR-homing according to the model. At a later stage, the larger nuclear-tipped Falcons substituted the rockets. The F-106 carried four Falcons and a single unguided Douglas Genie with a nuclear warhead. It entered service in mid-1959.

Lightweights

The F-101, F-102 and F-106 were all heavy fighters, illustrative of the pre-Korean design trend. That war showed the need for relatively small combat aircraft of extremely high performance, in order to win control of the air. The first result of this new thinking was the **Lockheed F-104 Starfighter.** The F-104 is an attractive, well-engineered high performance aeroplane, although it is a matter of opinion whether it really deserves the success that it has enjoyed. By the standards of the early Century-Series fighters, it is a comparatively light aircraft, due to its restricted fuel fraction and the fact that its basic armament was limited to the new six-barrel GE M61 Vulcan cannon (which operated on the Gatling principle) and two lightweight AIM-9 Sidewinder missiles. Infra-red homing produces extremely small miss distances, hence the warhead of such missiles can be very small, which results in a light weapon. The original AIM-9 weighed only 165 lb (75 kg).

Lockheed made a bold decision in adopting a straight wing, since in

An F-106A interceptor of the California Air National Guard launches a Hughes Aircraft radar-guided AIM-4F Falcon lightweight air-air missile from its ventral weapons bay during firing practice at Tyndall AFB, Florida. (Hughes Aircraft Co)

One of the most sensational fighters ever produced, the Lockheed F-104A Starfighter featured an afterburning General Electric J79 turbojet, a razor-thin straight wing, the new GE M61 20 mm Vulcan rotary-cannon and two wingtip-mounted Sidewinders. It also had a downward-firing ejection seat. (Lockheed Corp)

achieving Mach 2.0 performance this necessitated an extremely thin section (3.4 per cent), expensive construction, and a high wing loading. The engineering problems are well illustrated by the aileron jack, which had to be manufactured as a series of cylinders machined in a single slab of metal, in order to fit within the wing. The aircraft eventually grew to a weight of 31,000 lb (14,060 kg), giving a wing loading of 158 lb/ft^2 (772 kg/m^2), a figure that is unlikely ever to be exceeded by a significant margin.

It can be argued that the use of a straight wing was a mistake, since it produced a high landing speed, and required a high airspeed to achieve a useful turning performance. Although designed as a high altitude combat aircraft, the F-104 was probably best suited to the low level nuclear strike role.

The other design feature open to criticism was the high location of the tailplane. This gave rise to a pitch-up problem, and led its designers initially to specify a downward-firing ejection seat! This naturally proved unsuitable for low level escapes, and was quickly changed to a conventional seat.

Opposite left: USAF Starfighters in echelon starboard, a photograph that emphasises the anhedral of the wings. (Lockheed Corp)

The F-104A first flew on 7 February 1954, but persistent problems arose with this model, and most examples were exported. The USAF operated the improved F-104C in small numbers, and the type was deployed to Vietnam as an air superiority fighter, but it was found to be too short-legged to be useful over the North.

The only really successful version has been the F-104G, which incorporates a range of improvements and is fitted with a comprehensive nav-attack system. Its NASARR was one of the first fighter radars to provide a terrain-avoidance display. Powered by a 15,600 lb (7075 kg) J79-GE-11A

A Luftwaffe F-104G from JG71 'Richthofen', which in 1973 re-equipped with the F-4F. Note the characteristic cranked-up rear fuselage, to avoid ground contact at rotation and touchdown. (Roy Braybrook)

engine, the F-104G has an empty weight of 14,000 lb (6350 kg) and a maximum of 29,038 lb (13,170 kg). The F-104S is an even heavier variant developed for the Italian Air Force, with provisions for the AIM-7 Sparrow medium-range air-air missile.

Arguably how the Starfighter should have been designed in the first place, this Lancer projected derivative would have featured a low tail, and a high-set wing with leading edge extension. This layout would have avoided the F-104's pitch-up, which required a stick-pusher. (Lockheed Corp)

If the F-104 halted the upward weight trend of the Century Series, the **Northrop F-5** reversed it. Like the F-104, the F-5 has a straight wing, but it is proportionally larger and has a t/c of 4.8 per cent, limiting maximum level speed to Mach 1.4 in the F-5A series, and Mach 1.64 in the later F-5E.

In achieving the minimum possible weight for a supersonic fighter, Northrop exploited the high T/W of the General Electric J85 engine and the light weight of Sidewinder missiles. Unlike the F-104, the F-5 has two 20 mm M-39 cannon, ie, half the guns of the F-100. To save wing weight, the AIM-9 launch rails on the wingtips are located to act as anti-flutter weights, reducing the need for torsional stiffness in the wing.

The prototype N-156F flew on 30 July 1959, and the aircraft was (after some delay) selected as a MAP aircraft, the first YF-5A flying on 31 July 1963. The F-5A, equipped with two 4080 lb (1850 kg) J85-GE-13s, was later superseded by the F-5E with two 5000 lb (2268 kg) J85-GE-21s. This vastly improved model first flew on 11 August 1972. Although naturally providing less capability than much larger and more expensive fighters, the Northrop F-5 series have enabled many air forces to continue operations in financially difficult times, and have prepared pilots economically and safely for more potent aircraft. A total of 2,610 examples have been built, aside from almost 1,200 T-38 advanced trainers. The final F-5E was delivered on 16 January 1987.

This near-plan view of a CF-5A shows the Coke-bottle tiptanks and waisted fuselage, the inboard ailerons, early form of leading edge extension, and the flat base to the rear fuselage. (Northrop Corp)

Canadair-built Northrop NF-5As of the Royal Netherlands Air Force. (Northrop Corp)

The successor to the F-100 at the North American stable was to have been the F-107, an ill-fated project with a unique dorsal intake. (Rockwell International Corp).

An F-5E in USAF form, with enlarged leading edge extensions, Area Rule fuselage, and tip-mounted Sidewinders. The two launch rails are used as anti-flutter weights, to reduce the need for torsional stiffness in the wing. (Northrop Corp)

Short-Lived Successes

The **Republic F-105 Thunderchief** strike fighter was the heaviest single-seater used by the USAF, and it achieved an outstanding record in Vietnam. Designed originally to carry a nuclear store internally for high-speed penetrations, the aircraft was generally flown with an additional fuel tank in place of the bomb in the weapons bay. Capable of Mach 2.1 at altitude and Mach 1.1 at sea level, the F-105 was extremely difficult for defences to stop. Once external stores had been released and the nose was pushed down to unload the wing, nothing in Vietnam could stay with the F-105, since it would accelerate quickly to airspeeds that weaker aircraft could not tolerate.

Technical features included a moderately swept wing tapering from 5.5 to 3.7 per cent t/c, a sophisticated internal compression intake, convergent-divergent nozzle, and a dry wing to minimize the effects of combat damage.

The first YF-105 flew on 22 October 1955. There was then a delay while area-ruling was introduced on the fuselage, and the resulting prototype F-105B flew on the 26 May 1956. This model entered service in 1958, to be followed three years later by the F-105D with an advanced nav-attack system. The F-105D was powered by a single J75-P-19W giving a take-off thrust of 26,000 lb (12,000 kg) with afterburner and water injection. It had an empty weight of 26,855 lb (12,180 kg), a normal take-off weight of 35,637 lb (16,165 kg) and a maximum of 52,840 lb (23,465 kg).

Between 1965 and 1968 the F-105 dropped 75 per cent of the bombs released over North Vietnam. Production of the F-105 had ceased in 1964,

Above: The Fairchild Republic F-105 Thunderchief proved its excellence as a strike fighter in the Vietnam War. The F-105B illustrated here is distinguished from the later F-105D by the former's small radome. (Fairchild Republic Co)

however, and losses were running at more than 100 aircraft per year, hence it had to be withdrawn. Despite its strike role, the F-105 was armed with a 20 mm M61 cannon, and 29 MiGs were credited to the type.

The F-105's period of glory was cut short by attrition, but that of the **Lockheed YF-12A** was even shorter. Designed to perform a high altitude interception mission involving cruise at speeds in excess of Mach 3, the YF-12A first flew on 26 April 1962, and only three prototypes were built. Due to its speed and range requirement, it was a relatively heavy fighter, with an empty weight of approximately 60,000 lb (27,200 kg) and a maximum take-off weight of over 140,000 lb (63,500 kg). The YF-12A was powered by two Pratt & Whitney J58s of 32,500 lb (14,470 kg) thrust.

The wing planform of the YF-12A was a modified 60-degree delta with rounded tips, and large chines added to the fuselage and engine nacelles. It was 110 ft (33.5 m) long and 60 ft (15.8 m) in span. The fuselage chines each contained two Hughes Falcon missiles, and were cut back to clear the nose radome. Due to the cutback chines and large nose diameter (relative to the **YF-12C/SR-71** reconnaissance aircraft that followed), the YF-12A required a third and larger ventral fin, which had to be retracted sideways for landings and take-offs. Directional control was provided by two all-moving fins, which were canted inboard to reduce the rolling moments they produced. The aircraft relied on full-time stability augmentation, and a system that sensed the yaw produced by a drop of thrust on one side, and applied corrective fin movement. Longitudinal stability was modified by fuel transfer, to reduce trim drag.

Due to the high temperatures produced by flight at Mach 3, most of the structure was made of titanium, and the wing skin was given longitudinal corrugations to allow for expansion. To minimize fuel temperature problems, the wing tanks were used during the climb phase. Fuel was also used to pre-cool the compressor bleed air fed to the air conditioning system.

On 1 May 1965 a YF-12A established a series of world records, including a speed of 2070.1 mph (3332.3 km/hr) in a straight line, and a sustained altitude of 80,257.9 ft (24,469 m). In the event the requirement for a Mach 3 interceptor was dropped, possibly because the anticipated Soviet long-range supersonic bomber did not appear. The fourth aircraft of the series (the YF-12C) was built to suit reconnaissance duties, and this variant was manufactured as the SR-71.

Swing-Wings

Although less spectacular than the YF-12A, the **General Dynamics F-111** series has for many years provided the West with an essential supersonic nuclear strike capability. Designed to combine high-speed low level performance with unrefuelled trans-ocean ferry range and moderate airfield demands, the F-111 is a swing-wing fighter with a sweep angle variable between 16 and 72.5 degrees. It also has afterburning Pratt & Whitney TF30 turbofans, an escape module to rescue both crew members,

Previous page: Designed to fulfil a Mach 3 interceptor requirement, the Lockheed YF-12A first flew in 1962. Note that the fuselage chines are cut back to clear the nose radome, and that the fins are inclined to minimize rolling moment due to control deflection. (Lockheed Corp)

Previous page inset: A tanker's view of the YF12A, showing the combination of rounded delta and body-strakes. (Lockheed Corp)

The well-known SR-71A is effectively a modified YF-12 with the chines extended to the nose and the missile bays removed from these chines. The full-length chines eliminated the need for a centreline ventral fin. (Lockheed Corp)

The General Dynamics F-111A was the world's first variable-sweep production combat aircraft. Note the slats at the leading edge kink, to prevent flow separations. (General Dynamics)

and an internal weapons bay that will accommodate two bombs or one bomb and one M61 cannon.

The F-111A first flew on 21 December 1964, and was sent to Vietnam for operational trials during 1968, '72 and '73. The F-111 has been

The F-111F with what was presumably a trial installation of the Ford Aerospace Pave Tack IR detection and laser system, as used in the strike on Libya. (General Dynamics)

produced in six different models, including the F-111C for the RAAF, and the FB-111A for SAC. Typical of the TAC variants is the F-111D, which has an empty weight of 46,630 lb (21,150 kg) and a maximum weight of 100,000 lb (45,400 kg).

The F-111 was the first swing-wing production fighter. In the 1950s it was generally expected that, in order to restrict longitudinal stability variations, a wing would have to be 'translated' (ie, moved along the fuselage) as its sweep was varied. Computer studies by NASA, however, demonstrated that there was a locus of outboard hinge positions that would satisfy stability requirements. The F-111 was the first aircraft to make use of the NASA outboard hinge concept.

Navy Fighters

In this outline of the first supersonic fighter generation, priority has been given to USAF equipment because that service blazed the trail with the F-100, F-105, YF-12A and F-111 series. The US Navy came along later, partly because of fears concerning the practicality of operating fast jets from aircraft carriers. When they did eventuate, the early Navy jet fighters (with the exception of the F-8 Crusader) were less than remarkable, but then there appeared the F-4 Phantom II, which changed everything.

Grumman's first jet fighter for the US Navy was the straight-wing F9F Panther. Illustrated here is one of a pair of XF9F-2 prototypes, which were powered by Rolls-Royce Nenes, pending availability of the Pratt & Whitney J42. (Grumman Corp)

The Douglas Skyray had a delta wing with rounded tips. The faired noseboom on this F4D-1 suggests that it was the aircraft with the afterburning Westinghouse XJ-40-WE-8 that established a world speed record of 752.9 mph (1212 km/hr) in 1953. (McDonnell Douglas Corp) 1/43

Right: Marine Corps Panthers, evidently on the forward deck of the CV-42 (F.D. Roosevelt). The 'WP' tailcode indicates attack squadron VMA-223. (Grumman Corp)

At the start of the Korean War the US Navy was operating straight-wing fighters such as the **North American FJ-1 Fury** and **F9F Panther.** The appearance of the MiG-15 led to urgent developments with swept wings, including a navalized, cannon-armed Sabre. This culminated in the **FJ-4 Fury,** which first flew on 28 October 1954, with an enlarged wing and a t/c of only 6 per cent, an incredible figure for a subsonic aeroplane.

Other early swept-wing Navy fighters included the **Douglas F4D Skyray**, which had a modified delta wing with rounded tips, a t/c tapering from 7.0 to 4.5 per cent, and a 16,000 lb (7255 kg) afterburning P&W J57, but was still subsonic in level flight. It first flew on 23 January 1951.

On 7 August 1954 the **McDonnell XF3H Demon** had its maiden flight. By June 1955 the F3H-2 had a 14,500 lb (6575 kg) afterburning Allison J71, but was still unable to reach supersonic speed, notwithstanding a 6 per cent wing t/c.

Swept-wing development of the Panther led to the **F9F-6 Cougar,** which first flew on 20 September 1951, and then to the **F11F Tiger,** which followed on 30 July 1954. Equipped with a wing tapering from 6 to 4 per cent, an area-ruled fuselage and 10,500 lb (4760 kg) of afterburning thrust, the Tiger managed to reach Mach 1.1 at 36,000 ft (11,000 m). Some years later a Tiger (F11F-1F) was equipped with a 15,000 lb (6800 kg) J79, and reached Mach 2, but production orders were not forthcoming.

*Top: The McDonnell F3H Demon, although a forerunner of the
same company's F-4, gave little indication of the greatness to come. This
F3H-2N had limited all-weather capability, and was redesigned F-3C in 1962.
(McDonnell Douglas Corp)*

The Grumman F9F Cougar was the first swept-wing naval fighter to see active service, being used by the USN in Korea. Illustrated here is an F9F-8P with camera nose.
(Grumman Corp)

This remarkable underside view of the Cougar (possibly an F9F-8) illustrates its wing-body blending and the gradual fairing of the deep wing root into the rear fuselage. (Grumman Corp)

Below: The Grumman Tiger (exemplified here by an F11F-1) combined a thin moderately swept wing and an Area Ruled fuselage, making it the first carrier-based fighter with a level transonic performance. (Grumman Corp)

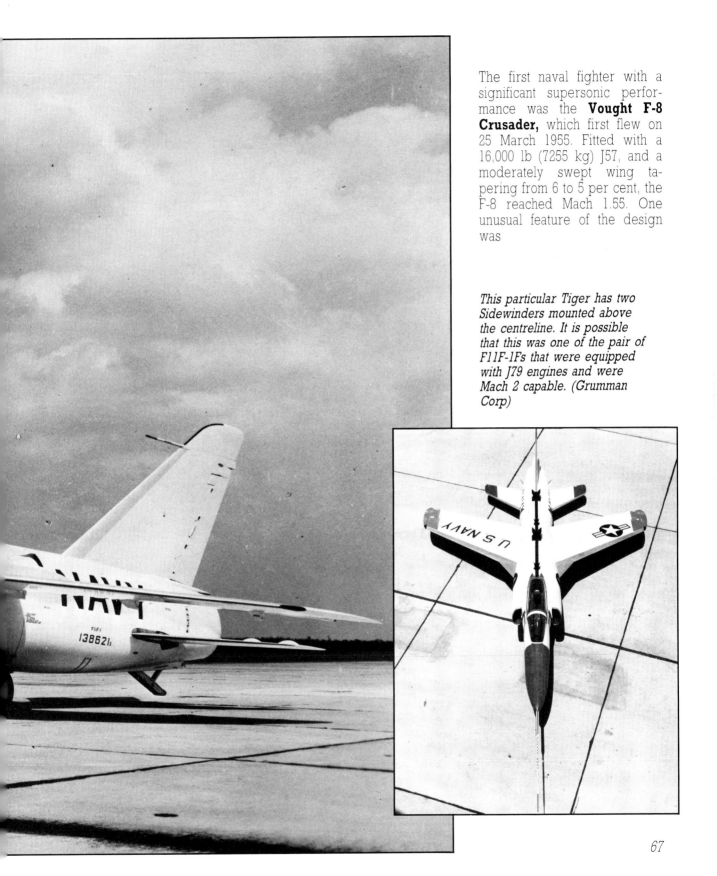

The first naval fighter with a significant supersonic performance was the **Vought F-8 Crusader,** which first flew on 25 March 1955. Fitted with a 16,000 lb (7255 kg) J57, and a moderately swept wing tapering from 6 to 5 per cent, the F-8 reached Mach 1.55. One unusual feature of the design was

This particular Tiger has two Sidewinders mounted above the centreline. It is possible that this was one of the pair of F11F-1Fs that were equipped with J79 engines and were Mach 2 capable. (Grumman Corp)

The variable-incidence wing of the Crusader is illustrated by this sole example of the two-seat TF-8A, formerly designated F8U-1T. (LTV Corp)

that wing incidence could be increased by 7 degrees by pivoting it about the rear spar attachments, in order to improve the pilot's field of view during launch and recovery. In Vietnam the F-8 was America's only simple, low-cost fighter suited to the air superiority role, and it acquitted itself well against the North's MiGs, destroying 19.

The USAF's main fighter problem in SE Asia was the lack of a long-range air superiority aircraft, arising from the fact that the emphasis had switched to carrying out and defending against nuclear strikes. The F-102 was restricted to the point air defence role. The F-104 could be used in dogfights, but lacked the range for operations against the North. The F-105 was limited to bombing missions.

The Vought F-8 Crusader was the world's first supersonic naval fighter. The F-8A (earlier F8U-1) shown here is one of a batch of 318. Total Crusader production was 1,261 aircraft. (LTV Corp)

Luckily, the Navy's **McDonnell F-4 Phantom II,** although designed for fleet air defence, proved capable of transition to the air superiority role. A two-man aircraft with a long-range radar, the F-4 first flew on 27 May 1958 and entered service in 1961. In the initial production series no guns were carried, but the F-4 had the outstanding armament of four semi-recessed AIM-7 Sparrow medium-range and four AIM-9 Sidewinder short-range missiles. This gave a combat persistence that was not to be equalled until the advent of the same company's F-15 Eagle in 1972.

The USAF adopted the F-4 for air superiority and ground attack duties, and combat demands in Vietnam led to the development of the F-4E with an M61 cannon under the nose and leading edge manoeuvre flaps. A more recent development is the F-4G Wild Weasel (defence suppression) variant. The F-4E has an empty weight of 30,328 lb (13,755 kg) and an internal fuel capacity of 1545 Imp gal (7023 litres). Maximum weight is 61,800 lb (28.030 kg); maximum speed is in excess of Mach 2.0.

Aside from being the multi-role hero of the Vietnam War, the F-4 has been produced in larger numbers than any other Western supersonic fighter. Its total of 5,197 units compares with the 5,600 of the F-86. McDonnell Douglas claims it was the first with a look-down, shoot-down pulse-Doppler radar (the Westinghouse AWG-10 in the F-4J), the first with significant structural titanium (7.5 per cent), the first with boundary layer control on both leading- and trailing-edge flaps, the first with drooped ailerons and slotted tailplane for reduced approach speeds, and the first

Left: The F-4E introduced a chin-mounted cannon and leading edge manoeuvre flaps, which provided higher buffet-free lift and reduced drag at high angles of attack. On test from St Louis, this F-4E carries EROS collision-avoidance equipment in the forward left-hand Sparrow groove. (McDonnell Douglas Corp)

Equipment updates are illustrated by this F-4E with Northrop TISEO (target identification system, electro-optical) mounted in the leading edge above the GBU-8 glide bomb on the inboard wing pylon. (Roy Braybrook)

One of the features that made the F-4 so remarkable was its air defence armament of four semi-recessed AIM-7 Sparrows and four pylon-mounted AIM-9 Sidewinders. This RAF Phantom FGR1 of No 111 Sqn, based at Leuchars, combines this load with three ferry tanks. (Crown Copyright)

capable of fully automatic carrier landings. Its two-dimensional multi-shock intakes with drooped lower lip and ramp suction are also worthy of record.

European Products

Only three European supersonic fighters of note were produced in the first generation. The **Saab Draken** first flew on 25 October 1955, and was noteworthy mainly for its double-delta wing configuration, with leading edge sweep angles of 57 and 80 degrees. Its bulged rear fuselage permitted an enlarged (Volvo) afterburner for its Avon engine, giving a thrust of 17,635 lb (8000 kg). In some respects the Draken was superior to the Mirage III, which had its maiden flight on 17 November 1956.

The unique double-delta planform of the Saab-Scania Draken is shown to good effect in this photograph of two Swedish Air Force J35Bs. (Saab-Scania)

Low aspect ratio wings result in high angles of attack at unstick and touchdown, hence the two small tail-wheels, which this J35F Draken is using as it touches down at a road site. (H-O Arpfors, Saab-Scania)

An RAF Lightning F6, armed with BAe Red Top missiles, equipped with a flight refuelling probe, and painted in air superiority grey, photographed at Binbrook. (Sgt J. Stubbert, RAF, Crown Copyright)

The **BAC Lightning** flew (in P.1B form) on 4 April 1957 and was powered by two afterburning Rolls-Royce Avons of up to 16,300 lb (7395 kg) each. The Lightning had an extremely high rate of climb and a useful ceiling, but exports suffered as a result of its relatively high price and limited multi-role capability. Like the Sukhoi Su-7, it had a highly swept wing, which made it difficult to locate stores abreast of the CG. Its interesting features were the sawn-off wingtip that eliminated torsional effects due to aileron deflection, and its unique vertical stacking of the two engines. This powerplant arrangement may have had some aerodynamic merit (in presenting the wing with a flat endplate), but the fact that no other company followed this lead probably indicates that the engineering problems were serious.

The **Dassault-Breguet Mirage III/5** series has unquestionably been the most important supersonic European fighter to date, although the French did not really pioneer the delta wing, the Mirage layout had

Dassault-Breguet pioneered the carriage of bombs on fuel tanks. This Mirage 5 has two 110 imp gal (500 litre) tanks, carrying four 500 lb (227 kg) bombs each. Total bombload is 7,500 lb (3400 kg). (AMD-BA)

serious drawbacks, and the results obtained by Israelis in Mirages fighting Arab MiGs have given a totally misleading impression of the aircraft's combat performance.

In terms of delta-wing pioneering, the Mirage III was preceded not only by the Convair series, but also by the Avro 698 Vulcan, which flew in 1952, and the **Fairey FD.2** research aircraft, which had its maiden flight on 6 October 1954. The FD-2 established a world speed record of 1132 mph (1821 km/hr) on 10 March 1956, a speed approximately equivalent to Mach 1.7, and 37.7 per cent faster than the record set by the F-100. The FD-2 was powered by a Rolls-Royce Avon RA.14R and featured a fixed two-shock intake, a 60-degree delta of 4 per cent t/c, and a 'droop-snoot' front fuselage as later used on Concorde.

It is part of British aviation folklore that the Mirage III was somehow inspired by the FD.2, just as its Cyrano radar was supposedly inspired by the Ferranti Airpass that went in the Lightning. In reality the first Mirage delta was the MD.550, which first flew on 25 June 1955, hence there was little opportunity for such 'inspiration'. Although of limited historical significance, the MD-550 was an interesting example of a lightweight fighter with a mixed powerplant, having two Viper turbojets and a SEPR rocket. In the early 1950s there was a wave of interest in mixed powerplants as means to achieve extremely high climb rates, another example being the **Saro SR.53,** which first flew on 16 May 1957. In the event, Britain chose to concentrate on afterburning turbojets, but France retained a SEPR rocket on some models of the Mirage III.

Before embarking on the Lightning, Britain considered combining turbojets and rocket engines, to produce fighters with outstanding climb rates yet reasonable endurance. One such project was the Avro 720, with an AS Viper turbojet and AS Screamer rocket. Some 85 per cent of the airframe was of honeycomb construction. (British Aerospace)

The Fairey FD.2 research aircraft set up a world speed record of 1132 mph (1821 km/hr) in March 1956, and may have encouraged Dassault-Breguet to develop the delta-wing Mirage series. (Fairey Holdings)

The first production version of the **Mirage** was the IIIC, which was an excellent high-altitude interceptor, entering service in 1961. At the time there was an element within the RAF that favoured having this aircraft instead of the Lightning but nothing came of this. The IIIE is a multi role version, while the Mirage 5 is simply equipped, and advertised as the world's least expensive Mach 2 fighter. The Mirage IIIE has a 13,230 lb

The ancestor of the British rocket fighters was the wartime Messerschmitt Me 163B Komet, which had a wing of 23 degrees sweep and two 30 mm cannon in the wing roots. (Roy Braybrook)

The only British rocket fighter to be flight tested was the Saro SR.53, which flew in May 1957. (British Hovercraft Corp)

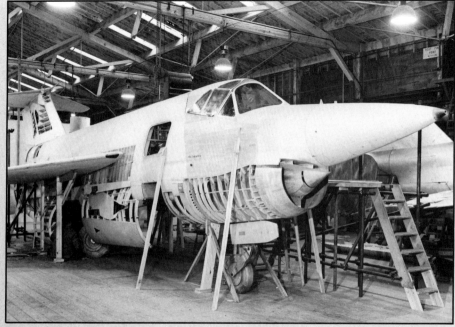

Shown here in mock-up form is the SR.177, a projected advanced derivative of the SR.53. (British Hovercraft Corp)

(6000 kg) SNECMA Atar 9C turbojet, an empty weight of 15,470 lb (7050 kg) and a maximum weight of 30,200 lb (13,700 kg).

The **Mirage 50** has a 15,800 lb (7200 kg) Atar 9K-50, while the new IIING has the same engine, leading edge root extensions, a small canard, fly-by-wire controls, and the latest nav-attack equipment. In all, 1411 aircraft of the first Mirage series have been sold, including exports to 21 nations.

There are two basic problems with the simple tail-less delta configuration. One is that the maximum lift coefficient is quite small, because the aircraft has no flaps, and since it is trimmed nose-up by means of a download on the elevons. The other is that sustained turn rate is extremely poor: pulling up the nose is like extending the world's largest airbrake.

The Dassault-Breguet Mirage IIING represents an update combining the Atar 9K-50 engine, canards, fly-by-wire controls, wing root extensions, and the latest nav-attack equipment. (AMD-BA)

Various attempts have been made to improve the aircraft. The manufacturer tested retractable foreplanes on the front fuselage of the Milan variant, but these necessitated removal of the nose radar. Israel introduced foreplanes on the intakes of the **Kfir-C2,** a locally-built derivative that was modified to take the GE J79 engine in place of the Atar. Canards were also tested on the Swiss Mirage IIIS, and they demonstrated

better yaw stability at high angles of attack (AOA), allowing minimum speed to be reduced from 150 to 107 knots (280 – 200 km/hr). Canard modifications for Mirage III/5 aircraft are being offered by both Dassault and IAI to existing operators.

Dassault-Breguet evidently decided at an early stage that the problems of a delta wing could best be avoided by reverting to a conventional configuration. The resulting **Mirage F.1** first flew on 23

Israel Aircraft Industries' Kfir-C2 has canards and the much more powerful General Electric J79 engine. Kfirs are shown here at turn-round on an operational airfield. (IAI)

December 1966, and deliveries began in 1973. At time of writing some 691 F.1s had been ordered by 11 nations. It is arguable that as a perfectly conventional aircraft the F.1 arrived on the scene very late, and that Britain should quickly have followed the Hunter with something like the F.1, but designed around the Avon used in the Draken. The Mirage F.1C is powered by a 15,875 lb (7200 kg) Atar 9K-50 turbojet, has an empty weight

The Kfir-C7 has two additional hardpoints, slightly more thrust, and a modernized cockpit. (IAI)

of 16,315 lb (74000 kg), a normal loaded weight of 24,030 lb (10,900 kg) and a maximum of 32,850 lb (14,900 kg).

In the late 1950s and early 1960s there was concern that the proliferation of Soviet tactical nuclear weapons (similar to those deployed by the US in 1954) would lead to airfields being wiped out in the first days of a European war. This led to efforts to develop dispersable V/STOL nuclear strike aircraft for NATO, a contest that was won technically by the

Hawker Siddeley **P.1154** and the Dassault-Breguet **Mirage IIIV.** However, the French were appalled by the cost estimates for dispersed operations, and Britain delayed the HS.1154 in a vain effort to satisfy both RAF and RN demands, finally abandoning the concept in favour of the F-4.

Sweden favoured dispersal, but could make use of straight stretches of highway, and thus did not need V/STOL. The generally favoured STOL approach at that time was the variable-sweep wing, but Sweden regarded such complexity as incompatible with dispersed operations. Instead, Saab-Scania developed a canard-delta configuration, in which vortices from the foreplane interacted with the flow over the main wing to produce a high lift coefficient. In addition, this arrangement allowed the use of trailing edge flaps on the wing, trimmed by flaps on the (fixed) foreplane.

The Hawker Siddeley P.1154
was to have been a supersonic V/STOL strike
fighter, powered by a Rolls-Royce BS.100
vectored-thrust engine with plenum chamber
burning. It is shown here in model form.
(British Aerospace)

The Dassault-Breguet Mirage IIIV was a more complex concept, with eight Rolls-Royce RB.162 lift engines and a SNECMA TF104 or TF106 for propulsion. First free hover took place on 12 February 1965. (Rolls-Royce)

These four JA37s, apparently a mixture from F6 and F15 wings, illustrate the cranked delta-canard arrangement of the Viggen. (A. Andersson, Saab-Scania)

The prototype **AJ37 Viggen** first flew on 2 February 1967, this first version being primarily for air-ground and air-surface use, with a secondary air-air capability. This was followed by reconnaissance models and the JA37 inteceptor variant, with a more powerful engine and the 30 mm Oerlikon KCA cannon, possibly the most effective aerial cannon in the world. The JA37 first flew on 4 November 1977 and entered service in 1980. It has a 28,110 lb (12,750 kg) Volvo Flygmotor RM8B turbofan engine, an empty weight of 26,900 lb (12,200 kg) and a maximum of 49,600 lb (22,500 kg).

Before leaving the subject of European developments, mention should be made of the more important fighter programmes that failed to reach fruition. In 1957 in the famous Duncan Sandys Defence White Paper, Britain decided that the only counter to nuclear attack was the nuclear deterrent, hence there would be no new fighters. The programme to introduce a new heavy all-weather interceptor (OR 329) based on a Fairey design was therefore abandoned, but as a cheap substitute the Lightning was developed from the P.1 research aircraft.

A second blow to combat aircraft development in the UK came in 1965, when it was decided to cancel not only the **P.1154** V/STOL tactical strike fighter, but also the **TSR.2** long-range strike fighter, a twin-engine aircraft in the 100,000 lb (45,400 kg) class, capable of bombing Moscow from UK bases. This was first to be replaced by Skybolt missiles on the Vulcan, and later (after Skybolt was cancelled) by various collaborative strike fighter projects, culminating in the Panavia Tornado.

The sole flying prototype of the TSR.2 at lift-off. (British Aerospace)

The JA37 interceptor version has a more powerful engine, the massive KCA 30 mm cannon in a ventral fairing, and provisions for the BAe Sky Flash missile, seen here on the outer pylons.
(A.Andersson, Saab-Scania)

Soviet Developments

Following the Korean War a number of important developments took place in the field of Soviet fighters, several supersonic projects making their maiden flights in the mid-1950s. The emphasis remained on the air defence role, although aircraft were switched to ground attack if it turned out that they were deficient in their primary task.

In chronological order of maiden flights, the first important supersonic Russian fighter was the **Sukhoi Su-7** (Fitter), which took to the air on 8 September 1955 and entered service in 1959. Like the Lightning, the Su-7 has a highly swept wing, but in this case the use of a single engine means that the wings are attached to massive ring-frames, rather than passing straight through the fuselage. It was the first Soviet fighter with a slab-tail and translating nosecone.

On 2 August 1966 a swing-wing derivative of the Su-7 began its flight tests, the aim apparently being to improve airfield performance while retaining a high penetration speed. This **Su-17** (also code-named Fitter) appears to have flown with a variety of engines from the 21,825 lb (9900 kg) Lyulka AL-7F to the Tumansky R-29 of up to 25,350 lb (11,500 kg). Despite its variable sweep, the Su-17 has up to 10 external load positions. Notwithstanding the age of the series, the Su-17 is still numerically the most important ground attack aircraft in the Soviet inventory.

The Sukhoi Su-7 was originally designed as a clear weather interceptor, but was soon relegated to ground attack, in which role its strong construction proved invaluable. (US Department of Defense)

The Su-17 is a variable-sweep derivative of the Su-7, and is shown here in the approach configuration. (US Navy)

The **MiG-21** (Fishbed) followed shortly after the Su-7, having its first flight on 14 June 1956. At the time it appears to have been Soviet policy to test new fighters with different wing planforms. In the case of the MiG bureau, the highly swept wing was abandoned, and the tailed delta arrangement was adopted. In the Sukhoi case, the highly swept wing was adopted for the Su-7 ground attack aircraft, and the tailed delta was retained for the **Su-9/11** (Fishpot) all-weather single-seat interceptor.

The tailed delta configuration was an important innovation, as it combined the wave drag benefits of the delta wing with the ability to use high-lift flaps. Other interesting features of the MiG-21 included a semi-encapsulated ejection seat, the cockpit canopy serving to protect the pilot from air-blast in high-speed escapes. This, however was later changed to a conventional escape system, because the initial concept was not suited to low level operations. The main undercarriage is wing-mounted, but articulated to position the wheels vertically in the fuselage sides. Both tailplane halves are actuated by a single jack mounted in the fin.

Rather like the Me 109, the MiG-21 has taken on heavy loads during its development, requiring powerplant changes from the Tumansky R-11 to the R-13 and ultimately the R-25, which have increased its thrust from 11,250 lb (5100 kg) to 16,760 lb (7600 kg). As in the case of the Su-7, provisions are retained for rocket-assisted take-off. Although a clever design for the point defence role, the MiG-21 is so small that it is widely regarded as a 'goes nowhere, carries nothing' aeroplane.

To counter such criticisms, the MiG bureau produced, in the early 1960s, a much larger twin-engined fighter of the same basic configuration, designated Ye-152A and code-named Flipper. No orders were forthcoming, since the Soviet Air Force chose the much heavier **Su-15** (Flagon), which has lateral intakes, permitting the use of a large nose radar. The Su-15 serves alongside the older **Yak-28** (Firebar) and the heavy **Tu-28** (Fiddler) in the all-weather air defence role. Meanwhile China, having copied the MiG-21 as the F7, appears to have completed development of the Flipper as the F8. The earlier MiG-19 has been produced in China in large numbers as the F6, and (with lateral intakes and an internal weapons bay) as the A5 ground attack aircraft.

In the same way that the Soviets made full-scale comparisons of wing planforms, they also compared the use of lift engines and swing-wings as a means of achieving STOL performance. The variable-sweep wing won the contest (lift engines are used only in the **Yak-38** (Forger) naval aircraft), and was applied to the design of the Su-17 discussed earlier and the **MiG-23** (Flogger).

A much larger and more flexible aircraft than the MiG-21, the MiG-23 has lateral intakes, permitting a nose radar. It began life with a 23,150 lb (10,500 kg) R-27, and graduated to the 25,350 lb (11,500 kg) R-29B. A distinctive feature is the massive leading edge extension on the outer wing. The **MiG-27** (also code-named Flogger) is a simplified ground attack variant with a laser ranger in the nose and fixed air intakes. Both models have a ventral fin that folds sideways for landing.

The Soviet equivalent of the YF-12A is the **MiG-25** (Foxbat), which achieves a similar speed capability using conventional aerodynamics, and steel rather than titanium. It is believed that this design originated as a

This Su-15 Flagon-F all-weather interceptor was photographed over the Baltic, armed with AA-3 Anab air-air missiles. (Swedish Air Force)

Right: The Soviet Navy's answer to the Sea Harrier, this Yak-38 combines a lift/thrust engine with two lift engines mounted just behind the cockpit. The aircraft in the foreground is armed with a gunpod on the wing pylon. (Royal Navy)

The MiG-23 Flogger, armed with two long-range R-23 (AA-7 Apex) missiles under the wings and two short-range R-60 (AA-8 Aphid) missiles under the fuselage. (US Department of Defense)

counter to the Mach 3 North American B-70 bomber, which was to have entered service in 1964, but was cancelled. The MiG-25 is thought to have flown at around that time, and was subsequently produced in both air defence and high altitude reconnaissance versions. Looking rather like an

A-5 Vigilante with sawn-off wings and twin fins, the MiG-25 probably falls short of the Lockheed aircraft in maximum speed, altitude capability and range, but is clearly a more practical shape for the fighter role.

The MiG-25M (Foxbat-E) is a converted Foxbat-A with more powerful engines and a limited lookdown/shootdown capability. It appears to be armed with four IR-homing AA-3 (Anab) missiles. (US Department of Defense)

To summarize, like the West, the Soviet Union discovered in the course of developing its first supersonic fighter generation that:
– an effective radar requires the intakes to be moved to the fuselage sides
– highly swept wings are beneficial for wave drag and gust response, but they result in high landing speeds and they limit the carriage of external stores
– variable-sweep wings are well suited to STOL strike fighters
– good warload-radius performance can only be achieved in an aircraft of reasonable size
– multi-role capability requires variable-sweep wings, or wings of moderate sweep.

One of the greatest fighters of all time, the North American F-86 Sabre was also one of the most attractive. This example (serial 51-12936) was the first of a batch of 34 F-86F-10s. (Rockwell International Corp)

The Dassault Mystere IVA was a contemporary of the Hunter, and superior to the British aircraft in certain respects. It was later used for weapon training, and replaced by the Alpha Jet. Here two Mystere IVAs are seen in formation with a pair of Alpha Jets (in the background). (Dassault-Breguet)

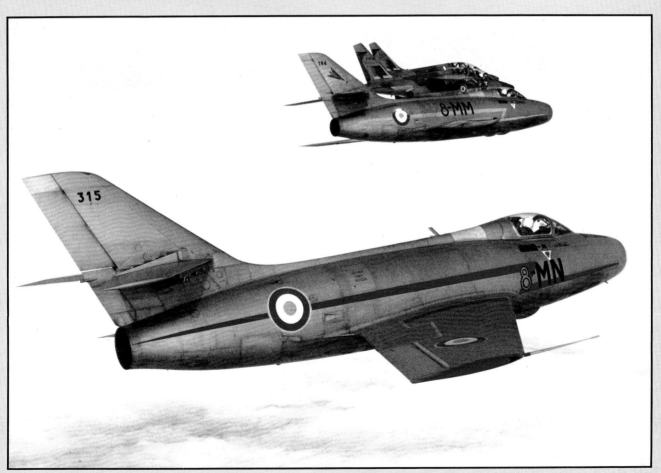

Top left: The first of the Century-Series fighters, the North American F-100 Super Sabre was the first aircraft in the Western world capable of supersonic speeds in level flight. (Rockwell)

Top right: A USAF Convair F-102 firing Hughes Aircraft Falcon air-air missiles from its weapon bays. (Hughes Aircraft)

Main pic: The Northrop F-5E Tiger II with a centreline pod housing a General Electric GPU-5/A 30 mm cannon pod. (General Electric)

Bottom: The Vought F-8 Crusader (shown here in two-seat trainer form) was the first naval combat aircraft with a worthwhile supersonic performance. Note the two-position wing, angled up 7 degrees for take-off and landing. (LTV Corp)

Above: McDonnell Douglas F-4B Phantom IIs of VF-101, an Atlantic Fleet Replacement and Training Squadron (as signified by the 'AD' tailcode), based at NAS Oceana. (McDonnell Douglas Corp)

Top centre: The BAC Lightning was the last supersonic fighter produced in Britain on a purely national basis. This RAF Lightning F6 (XR753/AC) was last reported with No 5 Sqn at Binbrook. (British Aerospace)

Top right: A fine example of a conventional multi-role fighter, this Mirage F1 carries the tiger's head insignia of SPA162, now incorporated in Escadron de Chasse EC1/12 'Cambresis'. (AMD-BA)

Bottom: A Mirage 5AD of the United Arab Emirates Air Force. (AMD-BA)

Main pic: The Mirage IIING (new generation) has the uprated engine of the Mirage F1, a foreplane, leading edge root extensions, and fly-by-wire controls. (AMD-BA)

What might have been the ultimate in strike fighters, the TSR.2 takes off on one of its few test flights prior to cancellation in 1965. (British Aerospace)

The McDonnell Douglas F-15 Eagle is currently the world's best day/night all-weather air superiority fighter. This example, judging by its 'LA' tailcode, belongs to the 405th Tactical Training Wing at Luke AFB, Arizona. (McDonnell Douglas Corp)

Test-firing of an AIM-54A Phoenix long-range air-air missile from a Grumman F-14A. The AIM-54 makes use of multi-stage guidance to permit firings at distances up to 100 nm (185 km). (Hughes Aircraft)

Probably still the finest long-range interceptor in the world, this F-14A Tomcat is seen with a full load of six Hughes AIM-54A Phoenix missiles. (Grumman Corp)

One of the first aircraft to enjoy a thrust/weight ratio in excess of unity, this F-15 is shown in a near-vertical attitude, armed with four AIM-7 Sparrow and four AIM-9 Sidewinder missiles (McDonnell Douglas Corp)

Chapter 2

The Teen-Series & Contemporaries

IN THE SAME WAY that the threat of the nuclear bomber and the air combat experience of the Korean War provided the main driving forces behind what has been termed here 'the obsolescent generation' of Western combat aircraft, America's Teen-Series fighters and their contemporaries were the result of several factors, including the 1965-75 Vietnam War.

However, in the course of the 1950s and 60s the whole business of planning military aircraft had become more formalized, hence computer studies and simulated air combats now played a major role in the development of the new concepts.

Once again, it is perhaps an oversimplification to regard those fighters that had their maiden flights during the 1970s as all belonging to the same technological generation. The F-14 and F-15 were planned before the Vietnam War had taught any new lessons about air superiority. They were F-4 replacements (one for fleet air defence, the other for day/night air superiority), designed around a new generation of high thrust/weight ratio engines. As it happened, the F-14 was rushed into the air so quickly that it arrived ahead of the new powerplants; and has consequently been stuck with comparatively old engines to the present day.

In contrast, the F-16 and F/A-18 resulted directly from the Vietnam War. The USAF, disturbed by marginal kill-ratios over the North, funded in 1972 a programme designated Lightweight Fighter (LWF) technology demonstration, which included the construction and testing of two General

Dynamics YF-16s and two Northrop YF-17s. Suddenly, in April 1974, the USAF 'shifted the goalposts' and the LWF technology demonstration became the Air Combat Fighter (ACF) selection programme. The YF-16 was running several months ahead, was less expensive, and offered engine commonality with the F-15. It won, but the twin-engined YF-17 went on to form the basis for the McDonnell Douglas F/A-18 for the US Navy.

To some extent the F-16 and F/A-18 thus incorporate later technology than the F-15 and F-14, although the latter pair, being larger, are far more capable aircraft.

Lessons of Vietnam

The air war over North Vietnam was quite different from that over Korea. Instead of USAF high altitude fighter sweeps being bounced by swarms of MiGs from even higher altitudes, it was generally a case of pairs of MiGs making slashing attacks against medium-level US strike formations, sometimes being intercepted by patrolling F-4 escorts, and occasional dogfights developing on a small scale.

Vietnam was technically interesting as the first war of any size to feature supersonic fighters, the large-scale use of air-air missiles, airborne fighter controllers in AEW aircraft, and the routine use of tankers. There were other innovations, such as real-time weather reports from satellites, but these were not primarily associated with air combat.

The radius of action used in attacks on the North was much greater than in Korea, the distance to Hanoi from Da Nang being around 350 nm (650 km) and that from Cam Ranh Bay being 600 nm (1100 km). The long distances involved were largely responsible for the extensive use of tankers. In the early days there were two daily tactical missions by the USAF against the North, each requiring the support of an average of 27 tankers. One tanker would typically refuel four strike fighters. These demands were in addition to SAC's own need to flight refuel its B-52s.

The enemy fighters encountered were mainly the MiG-17 and -21, although Chinese-built MiG-19s were introduced after the 1968 bombing pause. The MiG-17 (Fresco) was generally employed for airfield defence, using its guns, whereas the -21 was used in GCI sorties, making 6 o'clock attacks on US flights, and firing the short-range AA-2 (Atoll) missile at launch speeds around Mach 1.4.

The MiG-17 was extremely manoeuvrable, but in other respects was inferior to the F-4. The MiG-21 proved superior to the F-4 in manoeuvrability at low airspeeds, but the F-4 had better manoeuvrability and acceleration at high supersonic speeds. The F-4 was also better equipped and armed. Its radar would detect a MiG at around 30 nm (55 km), and its armament of four AIM-7s and four AIM-9s allowed it to engage the enemy at a distance of up to 10 nm (18.5 km) and down to an altitude of 1000 ft (300 m). The USAF began the war with the F-4C, which had only missiles, but the F-4D added a 20 mm ventral gunpod, and in 1968 the F-4E introduced the chin-mounted 20 mm (likewise GE's M61 Vulcan gun).

Air combats took place on a much smaller scale than in Korea. The

Fairchild Republic F-105Ds refuelling from a Boeing KC-135. The long radii of the Vietnam War placed severe demands on tanker assets, which were intended primarily for the heavy bombers of SAC. (US Department of Defense)

The boom-operator's view of
an F-105D Thunderchief.
(Fairchild Republic Co)

The MiG-17 was the Soviet equivalent of the Hunter, but it was used in Vietnam for airfield defence. These examples were built in Poland under the designation Lim-5. (Polish Air Force)

The MiG-21 has been one of the great postwar Soviet aviation successes, roughly comparable to the F-104. (Polish Air Force)

largest fight occurred on 2 January 1967 in Operation Bolo, when 14 flights of F-4Cs and four flights of F-104s, supported by six flights of F-105 Wild Weasels, carried out a mission over the North, simulating to ground radars an F-105 strike. The MiG-21s came up in pairs through the overcast and found, instead of bomb-laden F-105s, there were F-4Cs and F-104s with underwing tanks jettisoned, ready to fight. In the ensuing battle seven MiGs were shot down without loss to the USAF. For comparison, the largest air battle in the Korean War occurred on 4 September 1952, and involved 39 F-86s and 73 MiG-15s. On that occasion 13 MiGs were destroyed for the loss of four F-86s.

The most outstanding fighter of the Vietnam War was the Phantom II, seen here in F-4E form with chin-mounted M61 cannon. (McDonnell Douglas Corp)

The final air-air score was 193 MiGs shot down for the loss of 92 US aircraft, giving a kill-ratio of 2.1:1. Early in the war the exchange rate was more favourable to the US (it was 3.0:1 in the period April 1965 to June 1967), but it fell dramatically as the USAF began to bring in less experienced pilots (it dropped to 0.85 in the period June 1967 to March 1968).

In theory the USAF should have done much better, since its F-4s had medium-range missiles while the MiGs had none, but the reliability of early Sparrow models was low, and its use was restricted by the requirement (until 1972, when some concessions were made) for visual-identification of the target. This meant either that the attacking pair of F-4s needed another pair around 6 nm (11 km) ahead to identify the target, or that the attackers had to close in for identification, then fall back to fire. This restriction naturally reduced the opportunities for using Sparrow.

It is significant that the average kill rate achieved by both the Sidewinder and Sparrow was of the order of 10 per cent, although some sources attribute a figure of 20 per cent to the AIM-9, and something approaching 50 per cent for the -9G with a continuous rod warhead. Official figures are available for the period May 1972 to January 1973, when the AIM-7E-2 achieved 23 kills with 216 firings (10.6 per cent), the AIM-9E got six with 69 (8.7 per cent) and the AIM-9J got four with 31 (12.9 per cent). However, all these figures appear to be conservative, since missiles were often fired while the MiG was still out of range, simply to deter the enemy pilot from pressing home his attack on a US aircraft.

One important point that was subsequently borne out in combat simulation trials was that the use of semi-active missiles such as the AIM-7 placed an undesirable constraint on the launch aircraft, since it had to continue illuminating the target with its radar throughout the flight of the missile. Aside from its effect in eliminating other firing opportunities, this constraint also meant that the separation between the two aircraft continued to reduce, in principle allowing the enemy to respond with short-range missiles before being destroyed by the Sparrow. As a result of such considerations, it was decided to specify a fully-active ('fire-and-forget') missile to supersede the AIM-7.

Another important practical consideration that made the US superiority in air combat all the more remarkable was that the enemy enjoyed a considerable advantage in visual acquisition. Whereas both the principal MiG variants were small and smoke-free, the F-4 was comparatively large and produced two trails of black smoke.

The lessons of the Vietnam War thus amounted to the fact that the USAF needed aircraft capable of achieving air superiority at long range with the minimum use of tankers. They were to be armed with a mixture of medium- and short-range missiles, plus a cannon. They were to be as small as possible (bearing in mind the long radius of action required) and should have a clear exhaust. Since it appeared inevitable that some combats would always take place at short range, it was vitally important that US

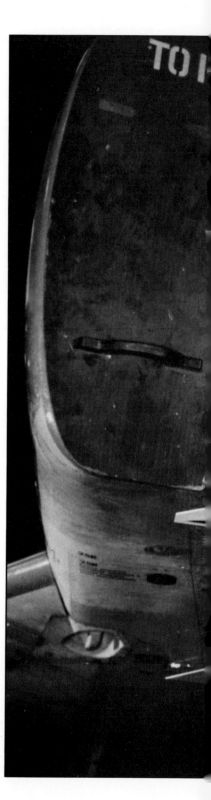

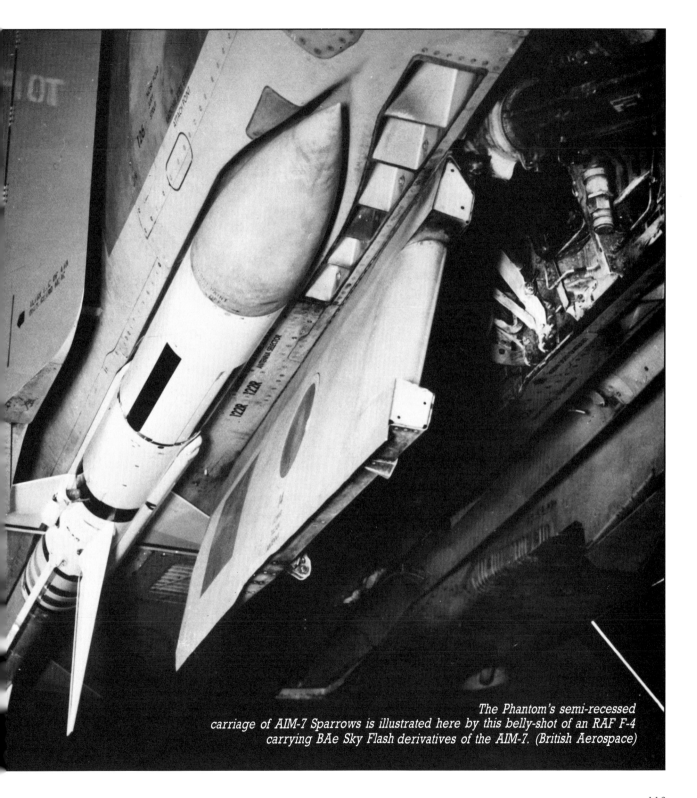

The Phantom's semi-recessed carriage of AIM-7 Sparrows is illustrated here by this belly-shot of an RAF F-4 carrying BAe Sky Flash derivatives of the AIM-7. (British Aerospace)

fighters should be able to out-manoeuvre those of the enemy.

During the time of the Vietnam War a great many computer studies were carried out to establish the relative importance of various performance parameters in a dogfight, the ultimate aim being to establish some 'air combat parameter' that would combine turn rate, acceleration, etc and thus allow different aircraft types to be compared with reasonable confidence. No such parameter has yet been widely accepted, but it is generally acknowledged that sustained turn rate in the transonic region is the most important single performance parameter. Nonetheless, maximum turn rate (ie, with speed decreasing) and specific excess power (ie, T-D x V/W) are also important.

Although it influenced directly only the later members of the Teen-Series generation of fighters, the Vietnam War was a crucial factor in the development of all these aircraft, since it illustrated the need to maintain a technological lead over the Communists, and it encouraged the spending of funds on the air superiority elements of the US armed forces.

Tomcat

For convenience, it has been taken that the present generation of fighters are those aircraft that had their maiden flights after 1 January 1970 and are now in service. Accepting this definition, the first significant combat aircraft of this generation is the **Grumman F-14 Tomcat,** which first flew on 21 December of that year.

The F-14 has been with us for some time (deliveries began in 1972), but the story of the project goes back much further, to the 1950s, when Douglas proposed a naval patrol-interceptor named the F6D Missileer. The F6D was to have been a heavy subsonic aircraft with a two-man crew in side-by-side seating, a large nose radar, and up to eight two-stage Eagle long-range missiles. It was to be powered by two conformally-mounted P&W TF30-P-2 non-afterburning turbofan engines. The F6D programme was terminated at the end of 1960, basically because it was a single-mission aircraft, and since carrier space restrictions militated in favour of multi-role equipment.

Although the F6D failed to win support, the Navy certainly needed an improved patrol-interceptor to counter the threat of Soviet stand-off missiles. In attacking carrier battle groups of the USN, it had to be assumed that the Soviets would launch cruise missiles from the radar horizon as seen by a medium-level aircraft, ie at a radius of around 200 nm (370 km). There was no hope of a fighter dashing out over this distance to kill the parent aircraft before it could launch its missile, hence the emphasis in specifying a new interceptor was on achieving long endurance. In order to provide operational flexibility, however, it was also essential that the same fighter should be capable of performing the air superiority mission, and of carrying out secondary missions such as strike escort and surface attack.

The obvious way to provide the desired operational flexibility appeared to be the use of variable-sweep wings. As it happened, TAC was

The Douglas F6D-1 Missileer was to have been a subsonic patrol aircraft, armed with up to eight Eagle long-range air-air missiles. (Harry Gann, McDonnell Douglas Corp)

simultaneously working on a requirement for a STOL F-105 replacement with a long range and a Mach 2.5 dash capability at altitude, a requirement that led to the F-111. Under the orders of Defense Secretary Robert McNamara, efforts were made in the early 1960s to combine the requirements of the two services in a single aeroplane, or two slightly

modified variants of the same design. The resulting **Grumman/Navy F-111B** first flew on 18 May 1965, but suffered a number of technical problems, including severe weight growth.

It became clear that there was no straightforward solution to the weight problem of the F-111B derivative of the USAF aircraft (the F-111A), so in October 1967 Grumman made a new proposal, retaining the TF30 engines and the avionics of the F-111B, but using a completely new airframe of much smaller dimensions. At a later stage this new aircraft

The F-111B in partially-swept configuration. Note the fuselage slot to take the variable-sweep wing, the spike of the quarter-cone inlet, and the translating cowl, giving an auxiliary intake slot. (Grumman Corp)

The General Dynamics/Grumman F-111B is shown here with its variable-sweep wings spread, in the loiter or approach configuration. (Grumman Corp)

117

(then designated VFX) was to be powered by the Advanced Technology Engine (ATE) that was being developed under joint USAF/USN funding.

Examining this new proposal, the Navy found the VFX to be superior to the F-111B, especially in what was termed the 'Other Fighter Role' of air superiority, and in May 1968 Congress terminated funding for the F-111B. Two months later the Navy issued an RFP for a new fighter to substitute for the F-111B, and in early 1969 Grumman was selected and contracted to develop the F-14A Tomcat.

Grumman was arguably the obvious choice for this task, having many years of experience with aircraft for the USN, and the best practical experience in the US (prior to the F-111) in the field of variable-sweep wings. Although America was the first country to make practical use of the swing-wing concept, the basic idea was developed first in Germany, from where this work was later taken over by Bell, and then by Grumman and General Dynamics.

The first variable-sweep aircraft was the Messerschmitt P.1101, although in that case the sweepback angle could be varied only on the

The first variable-sweep research aircraft of significance was the Bell X-5, based on the Messerschmitt P.1101, which had provisions for sweep changes on the ground. To maintain stability, the root of the X-5 wing translated fore-and-aft as it swept. (Bell Helicopter Textron)

ground. The P.1101 formed the basis for the **Bell X-5,** which combined wing sweep variation from 20 to 60 degrees with 'translation' of the mounting points along the fuselage. The X-5 was followed by the **Grumman XF10F-1 Jaguar** swing-wing technology demonstrator, which first flew on 19 May 1952.

The XF10F-1 provided useful background experience when Grumman was charged with responsibility for the naval version of the General Dynamics F-111, and work on the F-111B certainly helped Grumman win the contract for the F-14. Nonetheless full-scale development got off to an inauspicious start. The first prototype F-14A crashed on its second flight, due to loss of control power caused by fatigue failures in its hydraulic pipes. After this accident on 30 December 1970, the 10th aircraft was writted off on 30 June 1972 while the pilot was practising for an air display. On 20 June 1973 an F-14A flown by a USN crew was shot down by one of its own Sparrow missiles shortly after launch, though fortunately the missile was unarmed and the F-14 crew ejected safely.

In the course of 1972 the F-14A made its first carrier landings and catapult take-offs from the deck of the *USS Forrestal* (CVA-59). During the same year, deliveries began to the fleet readiness training squadron, VF-124, and the first two fleet squadrons. VF-1 and -2, were commissioned at NAS Miramar, California. The first deployment at sea took place in

The Grumman XF10F-1 Jaguar was virtually the prototype for a variable-sweep naval fighter, but it suffered various problems and series production could not be justified. (Grumman Corp)

September 1974, when these two squadrons were based on the *USS Enterprise* (CVN-65).

It was in June 1974 that the first of two contracts was signed (the second following in January 1975) for the supply of a total of 80 F-14As to what was then the Imperial Iranian Air Force. Deliveries took place between January 1976 and July 1978, giving the IIAF enough aircraft to form four squadrons. The motivation behind this purchase appears to have been to stop overflights of Iran by Soviet MiG-25 reconnaissance aircraft. In August 1977 live firings of Phoenix missiles were accordingly carried out by IIAF F-14As against high-flying Teledyne Ryan BQM-34E target drones, to spell out the risks associated with any further incursions.

Following the overthrow of the Shah in February 1979, the F-14As were taken over by the Iranian Islamic Revolutionary Air Force, but US assistance was terminated and with it the supply of spare parts. The F-14A has taken little part in the war with Iraq, which erupted in 1980, and it is believed that only about a dozen of these aircraft are still serviceable.

Returning to US Navy use of the F-14, the original plan was to buy 722 aircraft at a rate of around 50 per year. At time of writing the plan has been revised to 570 F-14As, followed by the production of 29 new-built F-14A (Plus) and 300 F-14Ds. It is anticipated that some of the original F-14As will be brought up to the A (Plus) standard to give a total of 70 to equip four squadrons.

The engines in the F-14A are Pratt & Whitney TF30 turbofans, the current standard being the TF30-P-414A, which has a dry thrust of 12,350 lb (5600 kg) and an afterburning thrust of 20,900 lb (9478 kg). In the F-14A (Plus) and F-14D the TF30 is replaced by the General Electric F110-GE-400, which produces 16,610 lb (7533 kg) dry and 27,080 lb (12,280 kg) with afterburning. The F-14D also has digital avionicss with improved ECCM and the ability to carry four AIM-120 (AMRAAM) medium-range missiles in addition to four AIM-54C Phoenix long-range weapons. Deliveries of the F-14A (Plus) are scheduled to begin in April 1988, with the F-14D following in March 1990. Aside from serving with operational USN squadrons, the F-14 is to serve with four Navy Reserve units.

The F-14 was the second production aircraft developed in the West on the basis of the NASA 'outboard hinge' concept. However, this application differs in a number of respects from the F-111. The sweep angle is normally set automatically in the case of the F-14, although manual control can be selected. The normal leading edge sweep angle range is 20-68 degrees, although an 'oversweep' position of 75 degrees can be commanded to facilitate hangar stowage. Another unusual feature of the F-14 is its 'glove vane', a triangular surface that extends from the leading edge of the fixed part of the wing. It is normally employed to restrict the movement of the aerodynamic centre in supersonic flight, and is fully deployed at a speed of Mach 1.5. Extension may also be commanded manually to make the aircraft more manoeuvrable at lower speeds.

This pair of Grumman F-14As from VF-84 'Jolly Rogers', operating as part of CVW-8 from CVN-68 (Nimitz) illustrate the side elevation and planform of the fully-swept Tomcat. Note the two AIM-54 Phoenix launch shoes under the fuselage. (Grumman Corp)

The F-14 has no ailerons, lateral control being provided by a combination of differential tailplane angle and wing spoiler action. For sweep angles above 57 degrees the spoilers are locked down, and rolling is controlled purely by the tailplane. The wing trailing edge flaps and leading edge slats are used to enhance air combat manoeuvring. Two vertical tails appear to be necessitated by the blanketing effect of the wide inlet ramps.

The engines are fed by multi-shock, two dimensional intakes that are set out from the fuselage to eliminate boundary layer problems. From the 68th F-14 onward, the TF30 was originally to have been replaced by the Pratt & Whitney F401 turbofan (the ATE referred to earlier), but this transition was continually deferred for budgetary reasons. However, the F401 was test-flown in an F-14A as far back as September 1973. Equipped with the 28,096 lb (12,745 kg) F401, the aircraft was to have been redesignated the F-14B, while the F-14C was to have been the same aircraft with updated avionics. Neither was funded, and the series will now go straight from the F-14A (Plus) to the F-14D.

The lack of funding for a more powerful engine has certainly restricted the value of the F-14, but what makes this aircraft the finest air defence fighter in the world is its combination of Hughes AWG-9 pulse-Doppler radar and the same company's AIM-54 Phoenix long-range missiles. The aircraft also has an M61 20mm cannon and provisions for Sparrow and Sidewinder. Possible missile combinations include six Phoenix and two Sidewinders, but a typical configuration is two Phoenix, two Sparrows and two Sidewinders.

Truly remarkable results have been achieved in the course of test-firings of Phoenix from the F-14. On one occasion a Phoenix was launched against a target simulating the Soviet Tu-22M Backfire supersonic bomber. The firing took place at a separation of 110 nm (204 km), and the missile covered a distance of over 70 nm (135 km) to intercept the target, which was flying at Mach 1.5. In terms of high-altitude intercepts, on another occasion a Phoenix successfully intercepted a drone simulating a MiG-25 flying at Mach 2.7 at a height of 81,000 ft (24,700 m).

Test-firing of a Hughes AIM-54A Phoenix from an F-14A. (Hughes Aircraft Co)

The capability of the F-14 system against a low level cruise missile was demonstrated by a Phoenix firing against a small target flying at an altitude of 50 ft (15 m) and a speed of Mach 0.75. However, the most important single feature of the F-14 system is its ability to deal with multiple targets. On one occasion six Phoenix were fired from an F-14A in a 38-second period against targets 30-50 nm (57-93 km) away. Four of the six missiles scored direct hits. Reports indicate that the overall success rate in USN firing trials of Phoenix has been approximately 84 per cent.

The F-14A has an empty weight of 39,760 lb (18,035 kg) and a maximum of 70,425 lb (31,950 kg). Maximum speed is Mach 2.34.

Eagle

Whereas the F-14 was developed primarily for fleet air defence, the **McDonnell Douglas F-15 Eagle** was designed for day/night all weather air superiority, with 'not a pound for air-to-ground'. At a later stage this emphasis on the dogfight role was to be relaxed to a significant degree, but the basic size and shape of the F-15 were determined purely with a view to destroying enemy fighters at long range.

Feasibility studies began in 1965, just as the Vietnam War was erupting. The F-4E was still three years from active service, but the USAF was already thinking of something far more advanced, a fighter that would provide twice that aircraft's rate of climb and acceleration, and half its radius of turn. Like the F-4E, it would have twin engines, but this new fighter would be a single-seater, using a new generation of radars and computers to eliminate the need for a second crew member. In 1968 the formal RFP was issued, calling for what was effectively an F-4E replacement to carry out the fighter sweep, escort and CAP missions. Strange though it may seem, this was to be the first completely new fighter designed to meet a USAF requirement since the F-101, which had first flown in 1954.

In December 1969 McDonnell Aircraft was selected to develop what up to this point had been termed the 'F-X', and early in the following year a contract was awarded for a preliminary batch of 18 single-seat F-15As and a pair of two-seaters, which were initially designated TF-15As and later F-15Bs.

The key to achieving a quantum leap in performance relative to the F-4E was the introduction of a new generation of engines, notably the P&W F100, producing a thrust/weight ratio of 8:1. This made it possible to design an aircraft with an unprecedented combination of T/W and fuel fraction. The very high installed thrust in turn made possible the use of a very low wing loading. In round terms, the initial aim was to achieve a take-off weight in the air defence role of around 40,000 lb (18,140 kg), with 50,000 lb (22,675 kg) of thrust. It was also expected to achieve a level speed of Mach 1.2 at low altitude, and a dash speed of Mach 2.5 at altitude. In the event, the weight target has been slightly exceeded, though in the short term (at least) weight growth will be offset by engine developments.

This pair of McDonnell Douglas F-15A Eagles bear the 'ZZ' tailcode of the 18th Tactical Fighter Wing, based at Kadena AB, Okinawa. (McDonnell Douglas Corp)

Take-off weight for an F-15A with four AIM-7 Sparrow missiles and full internal fuel is reportedly 41,500 lb (18,825 kg), and maximum take-off weight is 56,000 lb (25,400 kg).

Aside from the use of new generation engines, the next important step in the development of the F-15 was the selection of the Hughes APG-63 radar, providing a look-down, shoot-down capability. At the beginning of the F-15 programme it was planned that the AIM-7 Sparrow medium-range and AIM-9 Sidewinder short-range missiles would be augmented by a new cannon, the Philco-Ford GAU-7A. This was to have been a 25 mm gun optimized for the air-air role, and firing caseless ammunition. This revolutionary idea, based on bonding the projectile to a solid block of propellant, saves the weight of the normal shell case, and eliminates the time taken to extract the case after firing, thus permitting higher cyclic rates. With hindsight, it appears that the combination of a new calibre and a new ammunition concept was too great a gamble. Technical problems forced the cancellation of the GAU-7A, and the F-15 reverted to the well-proven 20 mm M61 Gatling gun, as used in the F-4E.

The prototype F-15A first flew on 27 July 1972, and the first production aircraft followed on 25 November 1974. Operational capability of the first squadron was formally declared on July 1975, and the first wing was fully equipped by the end of the following year.

Perhaps the most interesting aspect of the F-15 is that this aircraft is clearly the descendant of the F-4E. Although the wingtip shape has changed, the basic concept of a moderately swept, highly-tapered planform is still evident. The leading edge slats of the F-4E have certainly gone, but this is explained by the relatively low wing loading of the new aircraft, eliminating the need for really high lift coefficients. The new wing actually has some conical camber on the leading edge, which presumably gives part of the effect of slats, without the maintenance problems. The big change is the move to a high wing mounting, probably because McDonnell found it very difficult in designing the F-4 to get the tailplane low enough in relation to the wing. The adoption of a high wing made it easy to place the tailplane below the wing plane, although some price was paid in directional stability.

Another significant change was the switch from vertical to horizontal ramps in the intakes, in order to permit operation to higher AOA. An unusual feature is that the intakes of the F-15 pivot about the lower lips, to minimize spillage drag and the influence of the intake ramps on directional stability. In spite of this facility, the blanketing effect of these broad intakes still requires the use of two vertical tails. As in the case of the F-4E, the jetpipes are shortened, in this case with the tail surfaces mounted on two booms outboard of the afterburners. Another difference from the F-4 is that the F-15 pilot is set high in the fuselage under a teardrop canopy, giving an excellent all-round field of view.

One unique feature of the F-15 is the conformal fuel tank system that has been developed for some later models. Two tanks, each containing an additional 5000 lb (2270 kg) of fuel, can be attached to the sides of the fuselage with no reduction in the carriage of external stores. Another unusual feature is the use of a dogtooth leading-edge on the tailplane, evidently performing the same function as the inverted slat on the tail of late-model F-4s. Relative to the F-4, the cockpit is vastly improved, with an advanced HUD (head-up display) and HOTAS (hands-on-throttle-and-stick) controls, allowing the pilot to operate in a combat situation without removing his hands from the control column and throttle levers.

Construction of the F-15 is comparatively conventional, but titanium makes up 26.5 per cent of the airframe, mainly in the rear fuselage region. Graphite composites are restricted to 1.0 per cent of the structure, being used only in the airbrake and tail surfaces.

Although its wing area of 608 sq ft (56.5m²) is considerably more than the 565 sq ft (52.5 m²) of the F-14, the F-15 has begun life as a much lighter aircraft. It has (in F-15A form) an empty weight of 27,000 lb (12,250 kg), a clean take-off weight with four AIM-7s of 41,500 lb (18,825 kg) and a maximum of 56,000 lb (25,400 kg). As indicated earlier, it can attain Mach 2.5 transiently at altitude. Some indication of its climb performance was provided by the USAF 'Streak Eagle' project of 1975, during which an F-15 set new times to eight altitudes, breaking records previously established by the F-4 and (at the upper levels) the Soviet E-266, which is generally taken to have been a MiG-25. The times that beat the E-266 were: 122.94 sec to 39,370 ft (20,000 m), 161.02 sec to 82,020 ft (25,000 m), and 207.8 sec to 98,425 ft (30,000 m).

Aside from replacing the F-4E in TAC use, the F-15 is also replacing the F-106 in the defence of the continental US. Reports indicate that the USAF plans to procure an eventual total of 1,361 F-15s of various models, consisting basically of 969 of the earlier variants (F-15A, B, C, D) and 392 of the dual-role F-15E. The F-15C/D differ from the -15A/B in having internal fuel increased from 11,635 to 13,455 lb (5278 to 6103 kg), provisions for conformal fuel tanks, and a programmable radar signal processor, associated with a fourfold increase in computer capacity and the ability to track one target while searching for others.

The **F-15E dual-role fighter** is a two-seat day/night all-weather air-air and air-ground aircraft, derived from the F-15D. It will be able to carry external loads of up to 24,500 lb (11.115 kg). It will be equipped with the new Hughes APG-70 radar giving high resolution against ground targets, a central computer, programmable armament control system, updated electronics warfare system, provisions for the AIM-120 AMRAAM, a wide-angle HUD, and a system known as LANTIRN (Low Altitude Navigation and Targeting InfraRed for Night). The purpose of the F-15E is to augment the ageing F-111 in performing long-range, high-payload missions at night and in adverse weather. Maximum take-off weight is increased to 81,000 lb (36,735 kg). The first F-15E had its maiden flight on 11 December 1986.

The first export customer for the F-15 was Israel, which received 40 aircraft under the 'Peace Fox' programme. Japan is acquiring F-15s primarily by license manufacture by Mitsubishi. A total of 100 was planned

originally, but this has subsequently been revised to 174 aircraft by 1990. The Japanese programme is referred to as 'Peace Eagle'. 'Peace Sun' is the programme to supply 60 F-15s to Saudi Arabia.

Due to its outstanding performance, the F-15 provides a useful basis for a wide variety of tests. For example, an F-15 is being used as a launch platform for the ASAT (anti-satellite) weapon system, a two-stage vehicle weighing 2700 lb (1225 kg) and capable of intercepting targets at up to 550 km above the earth. Another F-15 equipped with canard surfaces and two-dimensional thrust-vectoring nozzles forms the basis for the SMTD (Stol and Maneuvering Technology Demonstration) programme.

The F-15 series has considerable potential for further development, partly because the F-15A/B began life with the first production P&W F100s. Major increases in engine rating are therefore to be expected. The current F100-PW-100 has a dry rating of 14,780 lb (6700 kg) and produces a thrust of 23,830 lb (10,800 kg) with afterburner. However, the F-15E has engine bays designed to accept growth versions of either the F100 or GE's F110, giving a thrust of up to 28,000 lb (12,700 kg).

Fighting Falcon

In contrast to the relatively large F-14 and F-15, which were conceived prior to Vietnam, the **General Dynamics F-16 Fighting Falcon** is a comparatively low-cost aircraft intended primarily for the daylight air superiority role. Conceptually, it might be regarded as 'America's MiG', although aircraft from that design bureau are no longer lightweight fighters. It could equally be regarded as the modern equivalent of two WWII aircraft: the Spitfire in dogfight capability, and Japan's Zero in terms of long-range air combat performance. Whether or not such analogies are accurate, the F-16 is undoubtedly one of the greatest fighters ever produced, in terms of its remarkable performance and its world-wide acceptance.

The USAF Lightweight Fighter (LWF) technology demonstration programme began in April 1972, and was the direct result of air combat experience in SE Asia. The service already had the F-15 under full-scale development (it was to fly three months later), but there was no way that such an expensive aircraft could provide the sheer numbers required to counter MiGs in daylight operations.

In investigating how new technologies might be employed to produce the greatest possible advance in air combat capability, the USAF funded General Dynamics and Northrop each to manufacture two prototypes that would incorporate all their latest ideas in airframe configuration, cockpit design and flight controls. The former company developed a single-engined aircraft around the P&W F100 used in the twin-engined F-15, while the latter developed a twin-engined design around the somewhat smaller GE YJ101. The GD YF-16 first flew on 2 February 1974, and Northrop's YF-17 followed on 9 June, a critical four months later.

Pressure was growing for the USAF to introduce as quickly as possible

The latest proposal for F-15 development is the SMTD variant, which will have two-dimensional nozzles and canards. Shown here in flutter model form, the SMTD will combine short field capability with 23 per cent more roll rate and 100 per cent increased pitch rate. (McDonnell Douglas Corp)

a fighter that would supplement the air superiority effort of the F-15, that would have outstanding dogfight capability, and that offered the prospect of matching Soviet MiGs in numbers. In April 1974 the USAF therefore changed the terms of reference for the LWF programme, transforming a technology demonstration effort into a direct competition for an Air Combat Fighter (ACF) that would be ordered in vast numbers.

In January 1975 the YF-16 was selected as the winner in the light of its performance advantages in acceleration, turn rate and endurance. It was also judged to have a better cockpit in terms of g-tolerance and all-round visibility. In addition, the YF-16 was felt to require less modifications to attain production standard, and to offer cost savings through engine commonality with the F-15.

The original production batch for the USAF was set at 650 aircraft over a five-year programme, which was linked to orders from the governments of the EPG (European Participating Group) countries, ie, Belgium, Denmark, the Netherlands, and Norway. In prospect were orders for 116 aircraft for Belgium, 58 for Denmark, 102 for the Netherlands, and 72 for Norway, giving an initial total of 348. In order to ensure that this contract was won for the US (rather than lost to Sweden's Viggen or some variant of France's Mirage F1), the second of the YF-16s was ferried across the Atlantic in May 1975 to be demonstrated at the Paris Air Show in the following month.

The dramatic demonstrations at Le Bourget were a major factor in the acceptance by the EPG nations of the F-16. Assembly lines were established at Gosselies to provide aircraft for the air forces of Belgium and Denmark, and at Schiphol for the services of the Netherlands and

In humid conditions, the manoeuvrability of the F-16 is dramatized by condensation from the fuselage strakes. The 'WA' tailcode of this aircraft indicates that it is part of the 57th Fighter Weapons Wing at Nellis AFB, Nevada. (General Dynamics)

This Royal Norwegian Air Force F-16A illustrates the clear-view canopy and wing-body blending of the Fighting Falcon. Note the parachute fairing at the base of the fin. (Roy Braybrook)

Norway. The EPG orders have subsequently been increased to 160 for Belgium, 70 for Denmark and 213 for the Netherlands.

The original USAF order for 650 F-16s has been left far behind, with a final total of 2795 now planned. The US Navy has ordered 14 F-16Ns for air combat training, and 12 more are expected to be ordered. Israel has bought 150, and plans a further 30. Egypt has ordered 80, with 36 more in prospect, Korea is firm on 36, but may eventually go to 156. Pakistan has purchased 40, and Venezuela 24. Turkey is to assemble 160. Greece has ordered 40 and may add a further 20. Singapore is firm on eight of the 20 planned. These figures give a planned total of 4092 F-16s, with funds already committed on approximately 3000 of these aircraft. By the end of 1985 around 1500 F-16s had been delivered to the first nine operators, ie, the USAF and four EPG air forces, and the services of Israel, Egypt, Pakistan and Venezuela.

This world-wide success is undoubtedly due to the F-16's unrivalled combination of performance and affordability. Like the F-15, its thrust/weight ratio and fuel fraction benefit from the use of the P&W F100 engine, providing a T/W of 8:1. The F-16, however, has many new features that enhance its manoeuvrability. Its relaxed static stability (RSS) allows the CG to be positioned well aft. In combination with synthetic stability and fly-by-wire (FBW) controls, this makes possible a trimming upload on the tail and a faster reaction to pitch commands. Manoeuvrability is also enhanced by automatically-positioned leading-edge flaps. Forebody strakes exploit the lift potential of the fuselage, and shed vortices over the wing that create additional lift and clean up the boundary layer flow, delaying the stall. Blending of the wing and body reduces drag and minimizes wing weight, by providing a deep structure to withstand bending moments. The ventral position of the intake makes it less sensitive to AOA than traditional side inlets.

All-round field of view benefits from the high setting of the pilot's eye-line relative to the upper fuselage lines, and from the absence of a windscreen arch. The pilot's g-tolerance is improved by a 30-degree seat-rail inclination and raised rudder pedals. The normal control column is replaced by a sidestick on the right console, which allows the pilot's arm to be supported in manoeuvres. There is virtually no movement in the sidestick, which acts as a force-sensing device. Longitudinal force inputs are transmitted to the flight controls as a g-demand at high speeds and as an AOA demand at low airspeeds. Lateral forces are sensed as roll-rate demands.

The current production F-16C has a wing area of 300 sq ft (27.9 m^2) and is powered by a P&W F100-P-200 afterburning turbofan of up to 23,830 lb (10,800 kg) static thrust. The F-16C has an empty weight of 17,960 lb (8145 kg), takes 6972 lb (2162 kg) of internal fuel, and has a maximum take-off weight of 37,500 lb (17,000 kg). It is designed to use positive load factors of up to 9g.

The F-16 has gone through various stages of development. The original F-16A has an empty weight of 16,236 lb (7363 kg) and a maximum

The unique canopy-cum-windscreen of the F-16 is shown in this 1980 photograph of GD test pilot Jim McKinney briefing Australia's then Defence Minister James Killen. The sidestick controller is just visible. (General Dynamics)

take-off weight of 35,400 lb (16,055 kg). It is equipped with a Westinghouse APG-66 radar. The F-16B is the two-seat trainer version of the -16A. Those F-16A/Bs that are in service with the USAF and the air forces of the EPG nations are undergoing an OCU (operational capabilities upgrade) programme, which includes provisions for the AIM-7 and Norway's Kongsberg Penguin III anti-ship missile, and preliminary provisions for the AIM-120 (AMRAAM).

The **F-16C** (and the two-seat -16D) introduce the GEC Avionics wide-angle HUD and the improved Westinghouse APG-68 radar. Later production F-16Cs can accommodate either the F-100-PW-220 or the slightly more powerful F110-GE-100 of 25,418 lb (11,525 kg) thrust. The

A F-16D with a GD-built reconnaissance pod, which would record a TV image of the area overflown on videotape, and transmit it to a ground station once sufficient height had been gained. The production model would combine several cameras with IR-linescan. (General Dynamics)

USAF is buying a mix of engines, but South Korea is adopting the F100, and Israel and Turkey the F110. The later F-16Cs will also have the ASPJ (Airborne Self Protection Jammer), GPS (global positioning system), and provisions for LANTIRN, the AGM-65D imaging-IR Maverick, and the AIM-120 AMRAAM.

Due in part to its FBW controls, the F-16 is a very flexible aircraft, of which several variants have flown. For example, the **F-16/79** is a two-seat version with the J79 turbojet engine, proposed as a low-cost fighter in response to President Carter's demand for an 'Intermediate Export Fighter' that would fall between the F-5E and F-16A in terms of cost and performance. The F-16/79 first flew on 29 October 1980, but no orders have yet been placed.

A more radical development is the **F-16XL,** which competed with the F-15E for the USAF dual-role fighter award. Proposals to manufacture the F-16XL as the F-16F were turned down, although the USAF representative spoke of possible future applications for the GD aircraft in single-seat form. Originally intended to explore the possibility of supersonic cruise without

afterburning, the F-16XL flew on 3 July 1982 in single-seat form with the F100 engine. A two-seat conversion has also flown, powered by the F110. Very little data has been released on the -16XL, beyond the fact that it has 85 per cent more internal fuel and 60 per cent less weapons carriage drag than the standard aircraft. Reports suggest it can cruise marginally above Mach 1.0 without afterburner.

Other variants of the basic F-16 include the AFTI/F-16, which is employed as a research vehicle under the Advanced Fighter Technology Integration programme. Easily distinguished by two canard fins mounted on nacelle hardpoints, and equipped with FLIR and laser sensors, this aircraft is investigating new methods of flight path control in air-air and air-ground attacks.

The F-16XL is a cranked-delta derivative of the Fighting Falcon, believed to be capable of supersonic flight without afterburner. The single-seat prototype is seen here in an air defence configuration. (General Dynamics)

Hornet

The **McDonnell Douglas F/A-18 Hornet** was an indirect result of the USAF LWF programme of the early 1970s, which led to the F-16. The aircraft that competed with the YF-16 for the ensuing ACF order was the Northrop YF-17, a twin-engined aircraft that first flew on 9 June 1974, the second prototype joining the flight test programme on 21 August that year.

Viewed as the basis for a production fighter (which was not its real purpose), the YF-17 was certainly short of internal fuel and lacked effective airbrakes, but it was nonetheless one of the most significant designs of the 1970s. The concept actually dates back to 1966, when Northrop began a series of design studies under the designation P-530. A much larger aircraft than the F-5 series, the P-530 had a high wing, though the straight planform remained virtually the same as that of its small predecessor.

Northrop discovered that a wing leading edge extension (LEX) not only improved the cross-section area distribution, but also created extra lift, due to a vortex shed over the upper wing surface from the leading edge kink. This concept was employed in various stages during the

The Northrop YF-17 lost out to the YF-16 in the lightweight fighter trials of 1974, but went on to become the basis for the McDonnell Douglas F/A-18 Hornet. This photograph shows the large slotted leading edge extension of the Northrop original. (Northrop Corp)

138

The Northrop aim had been to win funding for the P-530 Cobra multi-role fighter,
shown here in the form of the mockup that was displayed at Paris in 1973. (Northrop Corp)

development of the F-5 series, but it was taken much further in the P-530. By 1968 the design incorporated a large LEX and two vertical tails, which in the following year were brought forward to fill in the cross-section area between the wing and the horizontal tail. A period of design refinement followed, and by 1971-72 Northrop was proposing the twin-engined P-600 and the single-engined P-610 as contenders for the LWF technology demonstration programme. The P-600 was selected to form the basis for the YF-17, which was employed for the LWF trials and as the basis for ACF selection.

The large, subtly-cambered LEX of the YF-17 had a major effect on its lift characteristics. With zero flap deflection, it increased maximum lift coefficient from 0.9 to over 1.4. With LEX and manoeuvre flaps, lift coefficient at 8 degrees AOA was increased from 0.5 (for the basic wing, no flap) to 0.8. At 16 degrees, it was up from 0.85 to 1.4, an increase of 65 per cent.

The LEX also acted to reduce the apparent AOA at the intake face by directing the flow at the inlet. Whereas lateral intakes on a conventional aircraft at an AOA of 40 degrees would experience an apparent AOA of almost 50 degrees (due to upwash around the fuselage), the inlets of the YF-17 had an apparent AOA of only 25 degrees. At the same time, the fuselage boundary layer was sucked away through slots in the LEX roots by the low pressure created by the vortices. With most of the boundary layer removed, there was far less chance of flow separations ahead of the intakes.

The YF-17 also introduced the General Electric YJ101 engines, which had an afterburning thrust of 14,300 lb (6485 kg) and a bypass ratio of only 0.25. Aside from being remarkably tolerant of throttle mishandling, the YJ101 represented a break from the 1960s fashion of moderate bypass ratios, which gave excellent subsonic economy and a massive afterburning boost in thrust. The very low bypass ratio of the YJ101 gave a much higher non-afterburning thrust at high speeds (thus minimizing the use of afterburner) and a much lower SFC (specific fuel consumption) in afterburner. In a sortie involving significant combat time, the YJ101 thus showed major fuel savings, and in this sense it led the way for the fighter engines of the late-1990s.

Combining the effects of the LEX on the intake flow and the basic qualities of the GE engine, the YF-17 was flown to an AOA of no less than 63 degrees at a speed of only 20 knots (37 km/hr), and to a sideslip angle of 36 degrees in combination with an AOA of 40 degrees, without engine stalls and without departing from controlled flight. In paving the way for a new generation of fighters that normal squadron pilots could confidently fly to the limits, the YF-17 represented a major milestone in combat aircraft development. It had a take-off weight of 24,500 lb (11,110 kg) and a wing area of 350 sq ft (32.5 m²).

On the same timescale as the USAF ACF programme, the US Navy was looking for a new low-cost fighter (VFAX). However, the implication was that it would be rather larger than the ACF, since the Navy wanted a

multi-mission aircraft with an advanced radar. Aiming to save on defence spending, Congress terminated VFAX funding and directed the Navy to look at the YF-16 and YF-17. In making proposals for naval versions, GD teamed with Vought on the former aircraft, while Northrop teamed with McDonnell Aircraft on the latter. In due course the YF-17 was selected to form the basis for the new F/A-18, although McDonnell was appointed prime contractor in the light of the company's greater experience of naval aircraft.

The first F/A-18 Hornet had its maiden flight on 10 November 1978. It differed in many respects from the YF-17. The wing area was increased by approximately 12 per cent, to 396 sq ft (36.8 m²), to allow for increased weight and a slow carrier approach. The structure was generally strengthened for naval operations (especially in regard to the undercarriage), an arrester hook was added, and a wing-fold was introduced. The basic external shape was changed in three main respects.

One unusual feature of the F/A-18A is that the mainwheels are so far aft (as shown here) that the rudders have to be toed-in to facilitate rotation. (McDonnell Douglas Corp).

The radome was enlarged to take a 27-inch (68.6 cm) dish in place of the 23-inch (58.4 cm) antenna used in the design of the YF-17. A 'saw-tooth' was introduced in the wing leading edge. Finally, the LEX was enlarged and its shape further refined.

In the course of development to suit Navy requirements, the YJ101 engine became the F404, with bypass ratio increased to 0.34, giving an afterburning thrust of 16,390 lb (7433 kg). The internal fuel of the aircraft was increased from 6400 lb (2900 kg) to 10,860 lb (4925 kg). Empty weight was up to 23,925 lb (10,850 kg), and maximum take-off weight increased to 51,900 lb (23,535 kg).

The F/A-18 is said to be the first aircraft with digital quadruplex FBW controls, although mechanical back-up is retained for the horizontal tail, giving pitch and roll control in the event of battle damage. The F/A-18 remains a naturally stable aircraft, however, and it is claimed to have no AOA restrictions. Thanks to its straight wing, it has outstanding handling at low speeds.

Reports indicate that the F/A-18 is three times as reliable as the preceding F-4, and has only half the maintenance demands. Construction is relatively conventional, with 16 per cent of the structure made from steel, 13.3 per cent from titanium, and 9.5 per cent from carbon-epoxy. The very high reliability of the F/A-18 is partly related to its use of a new generation of avionics, including the Hughes APG-65 multi-mode radar. The facilities provided by the APG-65 include the ability to track 10 targets while searching for another, Doppler-beam sharpening for enhanced mapping, air-ground ranging, and terrain avoidance.

The first operational unit to receive the F/A-18A and two-seat F/A-18B (formerly designated TF/A-18A) was US Marine Corps squadron VMFA-314 at El Toro MCAS, California, where the Hornets began arriving in mid-1982, and operational status was achieved in January 1983. Following 11 test aircraft, the US Navy and Marines plan to acquire 1366 F/A-18s. Export orders currently stand at 138 for Canada, 75 for Australia, and 72 for Spain, giving a total of 1662 aircraft. Projected developments include a night attack version for the US services and a reconnaissance variant.

Hornets preparing for launch. Note that the ailerons droop in sympathy with the flaps, and that the rudders of the aircraft in the foreground are toed-in to provide a nose-up pitch as it clears the deck. (Northrop Corp)

Tigershark

Mention has already been made of the F-16/79, developed by GD in response to President Carter's call in 1980 for an Intermediate Export Fighter (F-X) to give a price and performance between the F-5E and F-16. Northrop's YF-17 and association with the F/A-18 led the company to believe that a good intermediate fighter could be designed around a single F404. This would give an initial thrust increase of 60 per cent over

An F/A-18A of VFA-125
'Rough Raiders' about to have
its nosewheel tow-arm
engaged with the steam
catapult. (Northrop Corp)

145

The Northrop F-20 Tigershark
with the General Electric
F404-GE-100 afterburning
turbofan that provided this
lightweight fighter with Mach
2 performance. (General
Electric)

the two J85s of the F-5E, and it was known to be a reliable engine with excellent handling characteristics.

 Although derived from the F-5E, the resulting **F-20 Tigershark** was virtually a completely new design. The basic wing planform was unchanged, though the skins were thickened to permit 9g manoeuvres at higher weights, and the LEX was increased yet again, giving a wing area of 200 sq ft (18.6 m²). The single engine is much slimmer than the two J85s in plan-view, but the rear fuselage was given a wide base by means of two 'shelves', to retain the high AOA characteristics of the F-5E. As in the case of late-production F-5Es, the nose was flattened to improve directional stability (the same effect being achieved in the YF-17 by means of small nose strakes). The tailplane was enlarged and equipped with FBW controls with mechanical back-up. A new canopy was provided with far better rear view, and the F-20 was equipped with the latest avionics, with emphasis on reliability and the shortest possible response time.

Test-firing of an AIM-7 Sparrow from an F-20. Such is that advance in powerplants and avionics that a massive punch may now be packed into a relatively small fighter. (Northrop Corp)

The initial production F-20A was proposed with the F404-GE-100 of 18,000 lb (8165 kg) afterburning thrust. With full internal fuel of 5050 lb (2290 kg)) and two AIM-9s, it was to have weighed 18,540 lb (8400 kg). Maximum take-off weight was 28,000 lb (12,700 kg). The F-20A would have had a maximum climb rate of 53,800 ft/min (273 m/sec) and a maximum speed of Mach 1.91. The first of three prototypes of the Tigershark first flew on 30 August 1982, but in November 1986 funding was terminated, due to the lack of a USAF launch order.

Typical of the latest fighter practice, the cockpit of the F-20 featured a head-up display, chin-level data-entry panel, two digital display indicator screens, and hands-on-stick-and-throttle controls. (Northrop Corp)

Tornado

The **Panavia Tornado** is an Anglo-German-Italian strike-fighter and patrol-interceptor that uses a variable-sweep wing to combine short field performance, high penetration speed and long loiter endurance. Originally designated MRCA-75 (multi-role combat aircraft for service in 1975), the Tornado is manufactured in different versions to suit different roles, and actually entered service in 1982. First flight of the basic IDS (interdiction/strike) version took place on 14 August 1974.

The underlying philosophy of the Tornado programme was to share development costs and to expand the production run. The initial orders for the IDS version were for 220 for the RAF, 212 for the German Air Force, 112 for the German Navy, and 100 for Italy, giving a total of 644 units. In addition, the RAF ordered 165 of the ADV (air defence variant), and nine attrition aircraft, the latter being combined with a contract covering eight ADVs for Oman, and 48 IDS and 24 ADV Tornadoes for Saudi Arabia. More recently, the German Air Force has ordered 35 ECR (electronic combat and reconnaissance) Tornadoes. The overall total of 933 aircraft includes four prototype conversions.

The basic IDS version performs the roles of close air support, interdiction, strike, and reconnaissance. It is reported to have an empty weight in the region of 30,800 lb (14,000 kg), full internal fuel equivalent to 11,250 lb (5100 kg), and a maximum take-off weight of 61,700 lb (28,000 kg). Aside from its variable-sweep wing, its performance benefits mainly from its highly economical Turbo-Union RB.199 turbofans, which use a three-spool arrangement to permit a very high pressure ratio.

The **Tornado IDS** has separate ground-mapping and terrain-following radars, and Doppler-inertial navigation. It mounts internally two 27 mm Mauser cannon, which have two selectable rates of fire to suit airborne and ground targets. Special air-ground weapons include two types of submunition-dispensers, the British JP233 airfield-denial system and the German MW-1, in which the submunitions may be chosen to suit airfield targets or groups of tanks. The IDS entered service with No 9 Sqn of the RAF and MFG-1 of the German Navy in June 1982.

The **ADV Tornado** is a patrol-interceptor for the RAF, derived from the IDS aircraft, with a different radar (the Marconi Foxhunter) to suit the air defence role, and a lengthened fuselage to provide more internal fuel and permit the carriage of four semi-recessed BAe Skyflash missiles. The prototype first flew on 27 October 1979, and production deliveries began in November 1984. The empty weight of the ADV is 31,975 lb (14,500 kg). Internal fuel capacity is 12,460 lb (5650 kg). Maximum take-off weight is unchanged from that of the IDS aircraft.

A German Air Force Panavia Tornado IDS fires its MW-1 munitions dispenser, which ejects laterally specially developed weapons for attacks on airfields or concentrations of armoured vehicles. (MBB)

Right: The RAF's Tornado F2 air defence variant with four BAe Sky Flash missiles in staggered array, and two Sidewinders cantilevered off the sides of the tank pylons. (British Aerospace)

The original ADV was designated Tornado F2 by the RAF, but most of these aircraft will be the F3 with extended reheat giving slightly more thrust. The ADV has automatic sweep angle control, and a slightly higher sweep angle on the fixed portion of the wing. Normal air defence armament is four Skyflash, four Sidewinders and a single Mauser cannon, but these missiles will later be replaced by the AIM-120 AMRAAM and AIM-132 ASRAAM. The ADV has demonstrated a patrol endurance of 2 hr 20 min at a radius of 325 nm (600 km) without flight refuelling.

Above: One of the most remarkable of Dassault-Breguet prototypes, the Super Mirage 4000 is a heavy multi-role fighter powered by two SNECMA M53 turbofans. In broadly the same weight class as the Tornado, it appears to have been aimed at possible Saudi requirements. (Roy Braybrook)

Mirage 2000

In seeking to replace the highly successful Mirage III/5 series, the Mirage F1 was too conventional to achieve large-scale success. However, when the F1 lost the competition with the F-16 in 1975 (for adoption by Belgium, Denmark, the Netherlands and Norway), Dassault decided to adopt the new technology of the F-16 and combine this with the traditional advantages of the delta wing.

Given relaxed static stability (ie, with the CG moved aft to an unstable location), the main disadvantage of the delta disappeared. Instead of high lift coefficients requiring a severe download on the elevons, they were trimmed with a useful upload. In consequence, approach speed was significantly reduced, airfield performance was improved, and the aircraft became far more manoeuvrable. The company made proposals along these lines to the French Defence Ministry, and the resulting **Mirage 2000** was officially accepted for development in December 1975. The first prototype had its maiden flight on 10 March 1978.

The use of artificial stability and FBW controls was the most important advance, in allowing Dassault to return to the tail-less delta configuration.

The Mirage 2000, however, also features automatic leading edge slats, which permit safe operation up to high AOA. In addition, there is considerable wing-body blending to minimize drag and increase fuel volume. Small strakes are attached to the intakes to improve directional stability. Some use is made of advanced composite materials, to save on structure weight.

The first production model was the 2000C, which entered service with the French Air Force in July 1984. The first 50 aircraft were equipped with the Thomson CSF multi-role radar (designated RDM), which is also fitted to export aircraft. Later French 2000Cs have the same company's pulse-Doppler RDI radar, which gives better air-air look-down results. The

aircraft is fitted with a duplicated Sagem Uliss 52 inertial navigation system. Recently offered is an avionics update, with a wide-angle HUD from the Rafale technology demonstrator and two TV-type multi-function displays (MFDs).

The second major version of this aircraft is the **Mirage 2000N** nuclear strike variant, which has the ESD Antilope radar and is armed with the Aerospatiale ASMP nuclear-tipped stand-off missile. It is the 2000N that has been the driving force behind development of the SNECMA M53 engine. The initial production M53-5 version was rated at 12,125 lb (5500 kg) dry and 19,945 lb (9000 kg) with afterburning, whereas the definitive M53-P2 is

Another elegant fighter from the Dassault-Breguet stable, the Mirage 2000 combines a number of interesting features, including wing-body blending, emphasized in this photograph of the first prototype. (Roy Braybrook)

rated at 14,335 lb (6500 kg) dry and 21,390 lb (9700 kg) with afterburning. The principal aim was to achieve a substantial increase in dry thrust, in order to improve the penetration speed of the 2000N.

It is anticipated that by 1988 French orders will total 243 aircraft, consisting of 139 Mirage 2000Cs, 19 2000Bs and 85 2000Ns. At time of writing, export orders stood at 36 for Abu Dhabi, 20 for Egypt. 40 for Greece. 40 for India, and 14 for Peru.

The nominal wing area of the Mirage 2000 is 445 sq ft (41.3 m²). Combat weight, which probably refers to half-fuel weight and basic armament, is quoted as 20,940 lb (9500 kg). Maximum speed is Mach 2.20.

Current Soviet Fighters

Very little is known of Soviet developments that might be described as contemporaries of the F-15, F-16 and F/A-18, although their basic shapes have been revealed by satellite photographs, and one type has visited Finland.

Two of the most important new Soviet combat aircraft (the Su-24 and MiG-31) actually belong to that period that bridges the gap between the two generations. The **Su-24** (Fencer) strike fighter first flew in 1970/71, and is thus a contemporary of the F-14. In terms of size and operational role, however, it is closer to the F-111, being a variable-sweep strike aircraft with a secondary air-air capability (in the context of interdicting air routes between the US and UK), and a maximum take-off weight in the region of 88,200 lb (40,00 kg). The Su-24 is believed to have entered service in 1976.

Another mid-generation aircraft is the **MiG-31** (Foxhound), a two-seat

Trials firing of a Matra Super 530D from the second prototype Mirage 2000. (SA Matra) 2/33

Above right: This MiG-31 was photographed off the coast of Finnmark by the pilot of an F-16 from No 331 Sqn of the Royal Norwegian Air Force in late 1985. (RNoAF) 2/34

The same MiG-31 seen from below shows the standard armament of four massive AA-9 missiles, which are believed to have a range of up to 24 nm (45 km) at altitude. (RNoAF) 2/35

derivative of the MiG-25, and the first Soviet fighter to have a true look-down, shoot-down capability. It is reported to have entered service in 1983 and to have a maximum speed of Mach 2.4. The engines are believed to be in the 30,000 lb (13,600 kg) class.

The **MiG-29** (Fulcrum) is broadly equivalent to the F/A-18, but it has a moderately swept wing and intakes that are well separated from the fuselage. Reports suggest that its two engines are Tumansky R-33Ds of around 18,300 lb (8300 kg) afterburning thrust. Six of these aircraft visited Kuopio in Finland in July 1986, but little was learned, beyond the fact that the main intakes are closed to prevent debris ingestion during the landing roll, and that the aircraft has a large IR sensor just ahead of the windscreen.

The **Su-27** (Flanker) is a much larger aircraft, broadly in the same class as the F-15. Nonetheless, it conforms to the same type of airframe arrangement as the MiG-29, with two fins and a moderately-swept wing, the fuselage located above the wing and the engines below, and well separated. In this case the nose undercarriage is much further forward, and measures to protect the intakes are probably even more necessary.

This slightly blurred photograph is the first available illustration of the MiG-29 with external armament. It appears to have two large AA-10 missiles on the inboard pylons and four short-range AA-11s outboard. (Swedish Air Force)

Chapter 3

The Next Generation

In considering how fighters are likely to progress beyond the Teen-Series and the Mirage 2000, this chapter looks first at the operational and political considerations that are pushing for a new generation, then at the various technological developments that may be exploited, and finally at specific future programmes and the experimental aircraft that are already laying the foundations.

It is arguable that, although America's Teen-Series and France's Mirage 2000 represent a broad spectrum of sizes and shapes, they are closely grouped in terms of technological timescale. This has allowed the Soviet Union to respond with its own new generation of fighters (notably the MiG-29 and Su-27) that may have arrived on the scene a few years later, but are dangerously close in overall quality to the West's latest in-service fighters.

Whether these new Russian combat aircraft are really as good as, or slightly inferior to, those of the West is virtually irrelevant in the present context. What matters is that Western air forces have to be able to win in a one-vs-many scenario, since it is inevitable that their aircraft will be outnumbered. In the case of the US, the whole operational philosophy of that nation's armed forces appears to be predicated on enjoying air supremacy. It follows that the West has to maintain a qualitative advantage and must find a means whereby its fighters can achieve a high favourable kill-ratio although outnumbered. In maintaining a significant edge, the advent of the MiG-29 and Su-27, broadly in the same class as the F/A-18 and F-15 respectively, justifies another massive leap forward in Western combat aircraft development.

It is only natural that Europe is in some respects ahead of the US in developing this new generation. America has made a large investment in its Teen-Series fighters, and is intent on achieving the maximum return on this funding through exports of the F-16 and F/A-18. In the same way, France has invested in the Mirage 2000, and would therefore like to see the next generation delayed until the late 1990s. On the other hand, the major advance provided by the F-16 and F/A-18 has given the US a virtual monopoly of the export market in the Free World. Unless Europe can respond with something that promises to leapfrog that generation, then its traditional markets may disappear for good, probably taking European fighter design capability along with them.

Britain is thus highly motivated toward launching a new generation, and is supported to some extent by Germany, Italy and Spain. France is in a more difficult situation, preferring a smaller aircraft on a later timescale to minimize the overlap with the Mirage 2000, yet not wanting to be left behind technologically. Dassault-Breguet had hoped to win leadership in a European co-operative programme, on the basis of the company's outstanding record of fighter developments. This, however, was an impossible dream in the light of the Panavia success story based on equal partners, and the fact that France already has a dominant role in Europe's principal commercial transport consortium, Airbus Industrie.

Further pressure for a new fighter generation came from Israel and Sweden, both of which have special operational needs, and aircraft industries that are highly capable and play a significant role in the defence of those nations.

Thus, there has been motivation since around 1985 for a new fighter generation to eliminate the threat of Soviet qualitative parity, and to safeguard the status of European industries, while satisfying local operational needs. From the user's viewpoint, however, how would the next generation differ from the last?

In the case of the US, the next generation is the ATF (Advanced Tactical Fighter), which is scheduled to replace the F-15. It may be recalled that the F-15 first flew during July 1972 and achieved IOC exactly three years later. By 1995 it will thus be 20 years since the USAF's principal means of achieving air supremacy entered service. Exports of the F-15 have been limited to Israel, Japan, and Saudi Arabia, and there appear to be no new prospects, although it is arguable that both Britain and Germany should have bought this aircraft. Deliveries of the ATF in the second half of the 1990s will thus come at a logical time in terms of the age of the F-15, and will probably have no impact on exports of this aircraft.

The ATF is expected to be broadly comparable to the F-15 in terms of size and weight, but it will differ operationally in at least three respects. Firstly, it is expected to have a useful supersonic cruise capability without afterburner, due to its low-drag shape and an abundance of 'dry' thrust. Secondly, it is anticipated that its design will incorporate the latest advances in stealth technology (including the use of passive sensors) in order to make detection difficult both for ground radars and opposing aircraft. Thirdly, the ATF will be much better than the F-15 at operating from bomb-damaged runways, thanks to its low wing loading, high lift devices, and its ability to vector thrust for take-off and reverse it for landing. In addition, the ATF is required to halve the maintenance demands of the F-15.

Whereas the ATF will be a comparatively large, heavy fighter providing air superiority at long range, the European interest is in a much smaller aircraft that is designed primarily for the dogfight role, but has a useful secondary ground attack capability. The basic philosophy is that the F/A-18 has more of a genuine multi-role capability than the F-16, and that the latest technology should make it possible for Europeans to duplicate the warload-radius performance of the F/A-18 in a somewhat smaller (and thus less expensive) aircraft.

Britain, Germany, Italy and Spain are currently working together within the Eurofighter consortium to develop a project that is termed EFA (European Fighter Aircraft). At the time of writing, France is pursuing its Rafale-B programme on a purely national basis, although it seems likely that some of the F-16 EPG nations (particularly Belgium) may join in at some stage.

The Eurofighter EFA and Rafale designs are markedly different from those of the F-16 and F/A-18, because those later aircraft are intended to make their kills in a new form of attack. As described earlier, the two US aircraft were a direct outcome of the Vietnam War, in which the vast majority of dogfights occurred at subsonic or transonic speeds. The F-16 and F/A-18 were consequently designed to produce the highest possible sustained turn rates under those conditions, the primary weapons being short-range missiles (eg, AIM-9L Sidewinder) and guns.

The new European philosophy is that the only way to achieve a high kill-ratio in a one-vs-many scenario is to exploit the full potential of medium-range missiles such as the Hughes AIM-120 AMRAAM. Aside from overcoming the traditional restrictions imposed by visual target recognition rules, this demands a radically different attack profile. The European fighter will thus detect and identify its opponents at long range, accelerate to a high supersonic speed in order to achieve the maximum possible firing range, and then (having salvoed its four medium-range missiles against up to four different targets) enter a maximum-rate turn in order to present the enemy with as difficult a target as possible. Any surviving opponents will then be attacked with short-range missiles (eg, ASRAAM) and guns.

The European fighter designer is thus concerned with a platform for four medium-range missiles in a low-drag installation (ie, twice as many as the F/A-18), with excellent acceleration to the region of Mach 2.0, and outstanding manoeuvrability throughout the speed range. His aircraft also requires very advanced radar, and cockpit installations to reduce the pilot's workload and increase his g-tolerance. Stealth considerations are probably less important than in the ATF case, since there is no suggestion of deep penetrations of enemy territory, and since high AOA operation and excellent visibility take precedence.

Configurations

If, as has been widely reported, the ATF is to employ supersonic cruise without afterburner, then very high priority must be given to reducing wave drag. This suggests the use of some form of slender delta configuration, as in the cases of the F-16XL and SR-71A, although STOL performance would then favour geometry variation, as would transonic and subsonic turning performance. These conflicting requirements may militate in favour of an arrowhead wing with variable sweep on the outer portion, but at time of writing the two shortlisted configurations have yet to be made public.

In the case of the new European fighters, the overriding consideration is to achieve a breakthrough in supersonic acceleration and turning performance. It appears to be widely (though not universally) accepted that the key to outstanding supersonic manoeuvrability is an unstable canard arrangement. This belief is based on computer studies and wind-tunnel research, possibly supported by data from free-flight tests with the Rockwell HiMAT (Highly Manoeuvrable Aircraft Technology) remotely-piloted vehicle.

For many years there has been interest in the idea of exploiting the canard arrangement's potential for STOL performance and turning flight, simply because a foreplane carries a trimming upload, whereas a normal tailplane carries a download. As described earlier, the Saab Viggen is a remarkable example of a canard configuration, developed to make possible STOL operations from dispersed highway sites. However, the current view is that in the case of a naturally stable canard its maximum lift is generally restricted by foreplane stall, since the canard surface is overloaded in comparison with the wing. What has made the canard attractive once again is the fact that unstable aircraft are now acceptable, due to FBW controls and artificial stability. If the CG is moved aft, producing instability in pitch, then the foreplane trimming load is reduced. This provides more scope for manoeuvre loads on the foreplane, and allows the full potential of the main wing to be used.

It is now being claimed that an unstable canard is equal (in manoeuvrability terms) to a tail-aft aircraft in subsonic flight, and superior above Mach 1.0. A canard aircraft also has a psychological advantage in the context of raising funds for a new development, since even a politician can see that such a layout is quite different from what has gone before. On the other hand, there is relatively little background experience with canard aircraft, which could still turn out to be a blind alley in fighter progress.

It has long been appreciated that, although a canard configuration may be the natural solution in designing a rocket-powered missile, it poses

One direct result of air combat experience in Vietnam was the General Dynamics F-16A Fighting Falcon. The 'HL' tailcode of these four aircraft indicates that they come from the 388th Tactical Fighter Wing at Hill AFB, Utah. (General Dynamics)

An F-16A of the Florida Air National Guard's 125th Fighter Interceptor Group, which is taking over some of the air defence role of the USAF's ageing F-106, with which it is seen here. (General Dynamics)

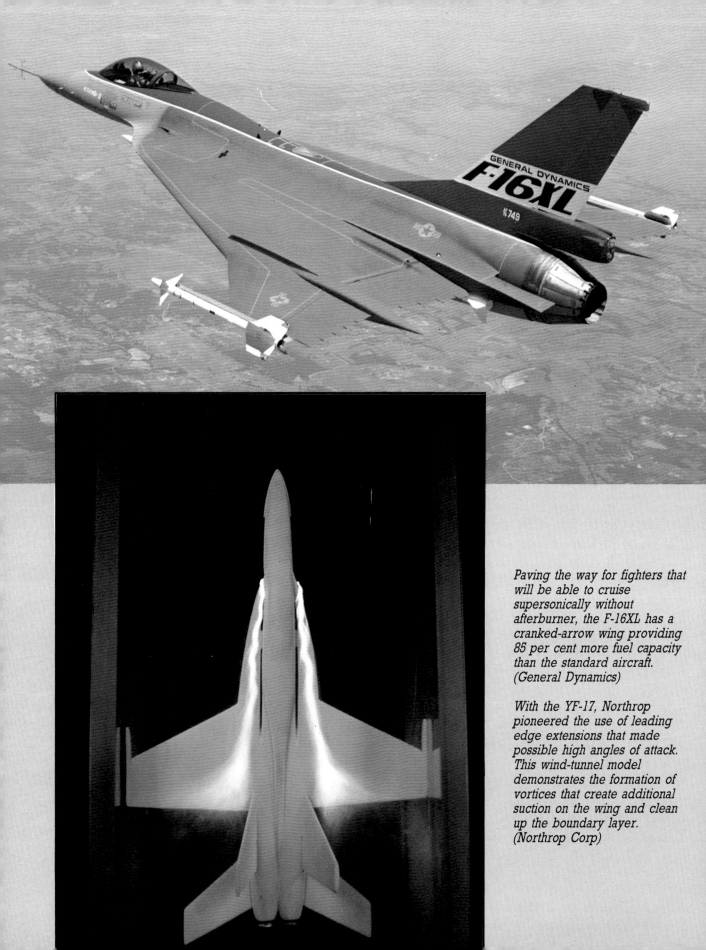

Paving the way for fighters that will be able to cruise supersonically without afterburner, the F-16XL has a cranked-arrow wing providing 85 per cent more fuel capacity than the standard aircraft. (General Dynamics)

With the YF-17, Northrop pioneered the use of leading edge extensions that made possible high angles of attack. This wind-tunnel model demonstrates the formation of vortices that create additional suction on the wing and clean up the boundary layer. (Northrop Corp)

The production derivative of the YF-17 is the McDonnell Douglas F/A-18 Hornet, seen here in US Marine Corps form, with two semi-recessed AIM-7 Sparrows and two wingtip-mounted AIM-9 Sidewinders. (McDonnell Douglas Corp)

One advantage of the virtually straight wing of the F/A-18 is outstanding handling at low speeds, which is vitally important in carrier landings. The 'NJ' tailcode is for VFA-125, the training squadron at Lemoore NAS, California. (McDonnell Douglas Corp)

The Northrop F-20 Tigershark lightweight fighter test-fires a Hughes Maverick air-surface missile. (Northrop Corp)

Pulling up at high speed over the sea, this Tornado of the Italian Air Force creates clouds of condensation over its fully-swept wings and contrails from the wingtips. (Aeritalia)

With wings swept at 67 degrees, this German Navy Tornado is configured for a high-speed strike mission, armed with four Kormoran anti-ship missiles. (Panavia)

The second prototype of the Dassault-Breguet Mirage 2000, pictured at Farnborough in 1980 in a long-range interdiction configuration, with bombs on the centreline, large auxiliary tanks inboard, and self-defence Magic missiles outboard. (AMD-BA)

First prototype of the Mirage 2000N nuclear strike fighter, armed with the Aerospatiale ASMP stand-off missile on the centreline. Note the small canards on the intakes. (AMD-BA)

The Sukhoi Su-24 (Fencer) is a heavy variable-sweep strike fighter, comparable to the F-111, but with a better secondary air-air capability. (Swedish Air Force)

Distinguished by canard surfaces on the intakes, the AFTI/F-16 was designed to explore new ways to fly and to attack air and ground targets. (General Dynamics)

The Boeing AFTI/F-111 is investigating the mission-adaptive wing (MAW) concept, which automatically produces a smoothly cambered aerofoil, optimized for speed and G-loading. (Boeing Military Airplane Co)

An artist's impression of the
F-15 STOL and Manoeuvre
Technology Demonstrator
(SMTD), with canards and
two-dimensional nozzles for
thrust vectoring and reversal.
(McDonnell Douglas Corp)

The British Aerospace EAP
(Experimental Aircraft
Programme) demonstrator,
fitted with mockups of four
AMRAAMs under the fuselage
and two ASRAAMs under the
wingtips. (British Aerospace)

The Dassault-Breguet Rafale-A technology demonstrator, armed with Matra Magic missiles on the tips and one 30 mm DEFA cannon in the left nacelle. Note that the intakes and foreplane position are completely different from those of the EAP. (AMD-BA)

An artist's impression of a BMAC concept for a future supersonic fighter, with wings of variable sweep and camber, two-dimensional nozzles, and conformal weapons carriage. (Boeing Military Airplane Company)

special problems when applied to manned aircraft with air-breathing engines, since the foreplane must be located where it does not interfere with the intakes, the cockpit, or the pilot's field of view. Another problem is that the canard aircraft CG is relatively well forward on the wing, hence it is difficult to place external stores where they will not create pitching moments on release.

In addition, the superiority of the canard evidently results from favourable interference between the two lifting surfaces, associated with vortices from the foreplane interacting with the wing vortices. Some designers suspect that this favourable interaction depends critically on the relative positions of wing and foreplane. In other words, an unusually high L/D may be created at the design point (ie, at a given Mach number and AOA), but under different conditions the advantage may disappear. There may be an analogy in effect to the laminar-flow wing sections used on some WWII aircraft, which gave very good results at the design lift coefficient, but no improvement under other conditions.

Among the European manufacturers there is considerable support for the ideas that the best wing planform is a compromise between a pure delta and a moderately-swept wing, the end result being some form of compound delta or perhaps an arrowhead. American designers appear to be more open-minded in their choice of wing planforms. Northrop, for example, still favours wings of very modest sweepback for some fighter applications, maintaining the pattern set by the F-5, F-20 and YF-17.

Grumman and Rockwell have both made detailed studies of the forward-swept wing (FSW), a concept that has rarely been tested full-scale. Of the few FSW aircraft that have been built, the general motivation has been to shift the wing carry-over structure aft of the weapons bay or passenger cabin. The FSW, however, may have a potential aerodynamic advantage over a conventional aft-swept arrangement, in that it may be more practical to suppress the characteristic root stall of the former than the tip stall of the latter. In principle, a foreplane may be used to create a downwash that delays the onset of wing root stall, hence there appears to be a possible argument for a canard aircraft with an FSW.

The traditional disadvantage of the FSW is that, in bending under lift loads, the incidence of the outer wing increases, creating additional lift, which in turn produces more bending and greater aerodynamic twist. The FSW thus needs enhanced torsional stiffness to control this tendency to divergence. Until recent times, the FSW has in consequence been significantly heavier than the equivalent aft-swept wing.

For completeness it should be added that the aft-swept wing reduces outboard incidence when bending under lift loads, thus shedding lift and creating a tendency to a combined bending/torsional oscillation. However, this tendency is easily cured by a slight increase in stiffness or by adding small inertia weights ahead of the torsional axis, an old Russian trick employed on the wing of the MiG-15 and the tailplanes of many later Soviet fighters.

Wind-tunnel testing in the US indicated not only that the FSW with a

One of the few vehicles to have provided free-flight test data on close-coupled canard arrangements is the Rockwell HiMAT (Highly maneuverable Aircraft Technology) RPV. (Rockwell International Corp)

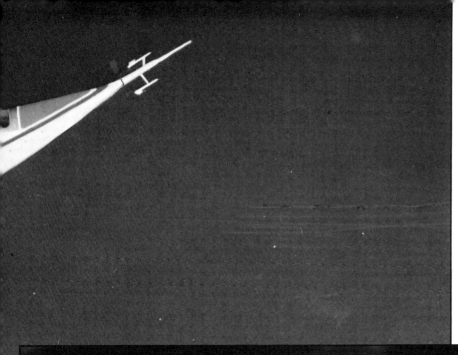

The Northrop/Dornier N/D-102 is a tactical fighter proposal combining a wing of modest sweep, two-dimensional nozzles, and no horizontal tail or foreplane. The philosophy is that thrust vectoring and reversal permits elimination of the tailplane and airbrake. (Northrop Corp)

foreplane could generate high lift coefficients, but also that this combination offered a major advance in terms of transonic L/D ratios. Grumman was responsible for a great deal of pioneering work in this area, and concluded that at around Mach 0.9 a high L/D required the maximum possible sweep at 70 per cent chord (where the upper surface shock sits) and the minimum sweep on the leading edge. This combination suggested the FSW. The company also concluded from free-flight model tests that the FSW with foreplane had an extremely high resistance to spinning.

The potential aerodynamic advantages of the FSW were thus well appreciated by some sections of industry, but the weight penalty remained. The structural breakthrough for the FSW came from Colonel Krone, USAF, who wrote a PhD thesis on the use of advanced composites in future aircraft. Since the material fibres can be orientated as desired in the construction process, the torsional axis of a composite wing is to some extent under the control of the designer. Krone concluded that this type of manufacture would allow wing-twist due to bending to be restricted, and hence that the traditional weight penalty of the FSW could be eliminated.

Some experts concluded that the FSW now offered scope for a significant reduction in fighter size and cost, especially in the case of an aircraft designed to perform a set-piece mission involving a relatively long time in transonic combat. In principle, a smaller wing would generate the necessary lift, and the thrust required would be reduced further due to the high L/D available. The concept was tested in the Grumman X-29 technology demonstrator. Although this aircraft has flown successfully, the indications now appear to be that the overall advantage of the FSW over a conventional layout is slight.

Aside from selecting a suitable planform, the designer can improve manoeuvrability through the use of some form of wing camber. Automatic manoeuvre flaps were introduced with the F-16, and are now virtually taken for granted. The next stage beyond having plain flaps on the leading and trailing edges is the Mission-Adaptive Wing (MAW) as developed by Boeing for application to a modified F-111. In effect, the MAW cambers the aerofoil in a smooth curve rather than a series of straight lines, giving a substantially higher L/D. The camber may also be varied across the span, to move the centre of lift inboard and thus reduce the bending moment at the wing roots.

No present-day discussion of the external shape of a combat aircraft can exclude some reference to 'stealth' or low observable technology, although very little authoritative information has been published on this subject.

The basic idea of stealth is to reduce significantly the probability of an aircraft being detected at a given range by any type of electronic sensor or the human eye. If in the first instance this discussion is restricted to radar, then the object is to reduce the aircraft's radar cross-section (RCS) and thus minimize the jamming power that must be incorporated in order that the aircraft can carry out its assigned mission. Jamming is, in any event, a somewhat dangerous procedure in a modern environment, since

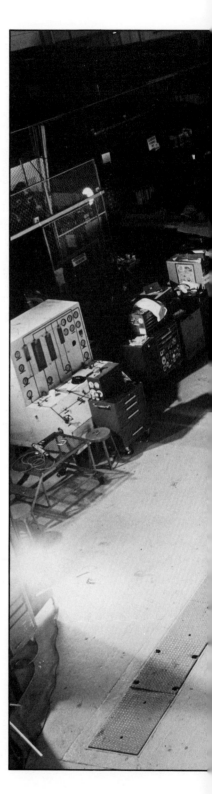

The Grumman X-29 forward-swept wing technology demonstrator, being prepared for structural testing. (Grumman Corp)

missiles are increasingly being given a home-on-jam facility.

It is clear that the aircraft's radar, IR and visual signatures will all be reduced if it can be scaled down in size. Not all means of signature-reduction are as obvious, however. In the case of radar, the situation is complicated by the fact that radar waves are returned to the transmitter not only by direct (specular) reflection from the aircraft surface, but also by travelling over the outer surface, and then scattering from a discontinuity such as the wing trailing edge.

In minimizing direct reflection, the airframe should consist of blended curves, the cockpit should be suppressed and the canopy coated in a reflective material such as gold, and the intakes and jetpipe nozzles should ideally be flush with the aircraft's upper surface. The intake ducts and the jetpipes should be coated in radar-absorbent material (RAM), and S-shaped to prevent sensors looking directly at the engines.

It is clearly preferable to carry stores internally, although historically this has seldom been favoured because of the associated loss of operational flexibility. If stores are to be carried conventionally, then a mid-wing location is better than a low wing, since the increase in side-view area due to the stores is minimized.

To avoid the worst peaks in RCS due to radar scattering at the leading and trailing edges, the wing planform should take the form of a continuous curve, rather than the traditional straight lines. Some reports indicate that RCS is also being reduced by having the wing edges skinned in composite material, supported on RAM-coated riblets that absorb the radiation passing through the skin. Recent advances in RAM, which in the 1950s was a thick rubbery material, may now allow it to be applied as a thin coat to external surfaces. In any event, RAM must be applied to the bulkhead behind the nose radar.

New Technologies

The radar aspects of low observable technology have been discussed first because they have a direct impact on the overall aircraft configuration. There are however, several other aspects to stealth.

Since the use of radar advertises the presence of the transmitter aircraft over a wide area, not only are special techniques being developed to minimize the information given to the enemy by a search radar, but also increasing use is being made of passive sensors such as radar warning receivers (RWR) and IR scanners. Very little has been published on the new radar techniques, but it seems reasonable to suppose that future combat aircraft will use their radars intermittently (relying on a memory mode for ground-mapping) and that, once a target has been detected, it will be tracked with short bursts of transmission, using just enough power to relocate it.

Passive IR sensors do not disclose the presence of the aircraft on which they are mounted, but they have the disadvantage that they can produce only bearing data, not target range. Nonetheless, they have been used for many years to supplement AI radars, and the current work on RCS reduction will clearly increase the importance of IR. An aircraft's IR signature is minimized basically by reducing the temperature of its exhaust gases, which suggests non-afterburning turbofans of relatively high bypass ratio.

Traditionally, IR acquisition range has been greatest from the 6 o'clock position, since the simplest (uncooled) sensors responded to the very high temperatures of the turbine blades, which can be 'seen' generally by looking directly down the jetpipe. This type of long-range IR detection can be eliminated by the use of an S-bend jetpipe, a feature that made the old Britannia turboprop a difficult target for first generation IR missiles. The IR signature of the Harrier series directly aft is reduced in the same way, and the emission toward the rear quarters may be screened by large stores on the inboard pylons. Modern IR sensors, however, tend to make use of the longer wavelengths associated with the lower temperatures of the exhaust plumes, providing all-aspect acquisition, although presumably at some-what shorter ranges than with first-generation lead sulphide cells. The longer wavelengths of cooled, second-generation sensors also rule out covert penetrations by supersonic aircraft, since the kinetic heating of the airframe can now be detected.

In the same way that stealth technology is encouraging the use of IR sensors, it is conceivable that at some stage sound-detection may be reintroduced to supplement radar and IR sensors. Noise signature, however, can be reduced by employing the smallest possible aircraft with non-afterburning turbofans of high bypass ratio, and sound-absorbent panels in the intakes and jetpipes.

Unlike sound-detection, visual acquisition from the ground has never been abandoned as a means of detecting and tracking aircraft in a jamming environment. In close-range air combat, visual target acquisition and tracking has always been essential, hence the reduction of an aircraft's visual signature is an important aspect of stealth technology.

The basic idea of camouflage is to break up the shape of the aircraft and to minimize its contrast with the background against which it is seen. During WWI there were various attempts to produce an invisible aircraft through the use of transparent coverings, but these appear to have proved unacceptable from weight, moisture tolerance, reflectivity and combat damage considerations.

The latest advance in the visual acquisition field is 'adaptive camouflage', a system which aims to minimize background contrast by sensing the intensity of illumination and lighting up the aircraft accordingly. In principle, this seems most appropriate to medium-range beam-aspect sightings, but there is no published information to indicate how successful this technique is in practice. In head-on acquisition at long range an aircraft is normally seen as a black spot, regardless of its actual colour, hence there may be a case for forward-facing lights, although these would presumably increase the chance of its detection at medium and short ranges. As in the case of radar, visual acquisition in precise side-view favours the use of twin vertical tails (canted inboard to reduce RCS), but in front/rear quarter-view twin tails probably provide more target area than a single fin.

Aside from producing an airframe with the best possible manoeuvrability and acceleration, and the smallest possible signature for various types of sensors, the fighter designer is (as ever) concerned with minimizing structure weight and production costs.

Since carbon fibres have much higher strength/weight ratios than normal metallic materials, it is widely accepted that future fighters will have large percentages of carbon composites, formed by placing layers of fibre tape on top of each other with resin between each layer. The highest carbon composite proportion to date is probably the 26.3 per cent of the McDonnell Douglas AV-8B structure, but new fighters are expected to have around 40 per cent of their airframes made in this way. The weight-saving on individual components is as high as 20 per cent.

In the very long-term future, small-scale use may be made of metal-matrix composites (MMC), in which filaments or whiskers of a high-strength material such as graphite, silicon carbide, or boron carbide are embedded in a ductile matrix of aluminium or magnesium.

The growing use of composite materials has encouraged the manufacturers of aluminium alloys to make major advances, notably with aluminium-lithium. This is approximately 10 per cent lighter and 10 per cent stiffer than the older aluminium alloys, and promises two or three times their fatigue life. In cases where these properties can be exploited fully, eg, in panels of the upper wing surface, the weight saving may be as high as 15 per cent. This is less than the potential saving with advanced composites, but it is achieved using existing types of machinery and without the need for special training for the work-force.

Looking further into the future, high temperature alloys of aluminium are being developed, using iron and cerium to produce metals that are just as suitable as titanium for high-Mach applications, but offering weight savings of around 15 per cent and cost savings in the region of 65 per cent.

Although composite materials are intended primarily to save weight, it is felt that automation will eventually permit manufacturing costs to be reduced below current levels for metal fabrication. Other cost-reduction developments include superplastic forming (SPF), which allows complex shapes to be produced in single pieces of titanium, aluminium or aluminium lithium alloys, and the diffusion-bonding (DB) of titanium components.

Powerplants

Whereas the majority of existing fighters (with the noteworthy exception of the F/A-18) are powered by turbofans of moderately high bypass ratio, since this characteristic produces a massive thrust boost when the afterburner is ignited, combined with low fuel consumption in subsonic cruise, the next generation will have engines of low bypass ratio. This type of turbofan, sometimes referrred to as a 'leaky turbojet', gives proportionally much more dry (ie, non-afterburning) thrust at high speeds, and a far lower specific fuel consumption (SFC) in afterburner. In essence, the last fighter generation was designed for loiter performance in a patrol-intercept mission, and the next generation is expected to fight for its life from the minute the gear is up. In combination with an airframe of very low wave drag, such engines will also permit some degree of supersonic cruise without afterburner.

Since there is a clear conflict between subsonic demands for high bypass and supersonic demands for low bypass, it seems inevitable that at some stage fighters will have variable-cycle engines that can somehow change their bypass ratios to suit each phase of the sortie.

In the short term, the emphasis is on combining very high thrust/weight ratios with bypass ratios below 0.5:1, digital controls, and achieving current pressure ratios with less compressor stages and less blades per stage. Today's advanced engines give thrust/weight ratios of around 8:1, but the 1990s will see values of 10:1, and the early years of the next century will witness ratios of 12:1. As a result, fighters will have proportionally more thrust for less powerplant weight.

One of the most useful powerplant advances available in the relatively near future is the use of thrust-vectoring in the context of afterburning engines. To date the only practical application of thrust-vectoring has been in the case of the Rolls-Royce Pegasus series for the Harrier V/STOL family, but it is now appreciated that this concept can also be applied to

more conventional combat aircraft. Whereas in the Harrier/Pegasus combination the thrust line always passes through the aircraft CG, thrust-vectoring in a conventional fighter implies variable geometry at the rear end, and hence pitching moments. In the context of a simple pilot-operated system, this sounded dangerous. Operated via an autopilot, however, such a system offered the prospect of rapid response in pitch for combat manoeuvres, safety in high-AOA operation, and the possibility of short take-off by pitching the aircraft up to an attitude at which the vertical component of its thrust would usefully reduce the weight that its wings had to support.

Although 'bending' afterburners were schemed for V/STOL applications in the 1960s, it is now felt that this type of thrust-vectoring necessitates two-dimensional nozzles, ie, rectangular cross-sections, rather than the normal circular shapes. Pratt & Whitney has developed such a 2-D nozzle for the F100 engine, and this is being tested on a modified F-15. This technology demonstrator nozzle also provides thrust reversal on the ground, to minimize ground run.

Looking further into the future, it is conceivable that fighters may be able to use thrust reversal in combat to force a pursuing enemy aircraft to overshoot into a vulnerable position, although this would clearly be a last-ditch manoeuvre. In-flight thrust reversal (which is used on some commercial transports, notably the DC-8) was considered during the design of the Saab Viggen, and might be tested on this aircraft or the Panavia Tornado, given suitable strengthening. There have been reports that this facility may be introduced at some stage of the Eurofighter EFA programme, a consideration that may have encouraged the use of a single fin in place of the original twin-tails. Up to the present time, however, the only full-scale trials of in-flight thrust-reversal on a fighter have been those on a Grumman F-11F Tiger some years ago, using a Rohr-built reverser on its Wright J65.

Thrust reversal in combat may be likened to using a large and invisible airbrake, but it will result in the aircraft losing so much energy

Mock-up of the Pratt & Whitney PX5000 turbofan engine (now designated YF119) with two-dimensional nozzle for thrust-vectoring and reversal. This engine is competing with the General Electric GE37 (YF120) for the USAF ATF order. (Pratt & Whitney Aircraft)

that it will take a substantial time to regain manoeuvring speed. There are several other new types of flight path control that appear to be more promising, although some of these innovations require additional control surfaces. The most popular ideas appear to centre on generating a force through the CG to modify the aircraft's flight path without changing its attitude, using direct lift control (DLC) or direct side-force control (DSFC). Computer studies have indicated that these control concepts could increase hit probability in dive attacks against ground targets by the order of 50 per cent. Another potentially useful innovation is the linking of the radar-based fire control system to the flight controls for increased accuracy in air-air gun attacks.

Cockpits

A great deal of thought is being directed toward improved cockpits, in

The cockpit of the AFTI/F-16 combines a wide-angle head-up display (by GEC Avionics) with two head-down multi-function TV-type displays, which can show flight and navigation information or the pictures produced by sensors on the aircraft and its weapons. The HUD can display a FLIR picture, making possible low level operations at night. (General Dynamics)

order to make the pilot more effective while decreasing his workload.

One way to improve pilot efficiency is to increase g-tolerance. This may be done by increasing the inclination of the seat, but extreme angles make it difficult for him to see the instruments and may pose problems with fin-clearance on ejection. Future seats may have some form of geometry variation, such as inflatable cushions and tilting headrests. To improve survival chances, seats may well have vertical-sensing devices to permit low level ejections despite significant bank and pitch angles.

The ability of the latest missiles to engage targets at large angles off the aircraft's line of flight demands a helmet-mounted sight (HMS), since even a wide-angle head-up display (HUD) presents too small a field of view. Once the pilot's visor is used to provide an aiming marker, it is only a short step to developing a helmet-mounted display (HMD), showing most of the information normally presented on a fixed HUD. The visor will also be coated to protect the pilot from laser beams and nuclear flash.

In the present generation the HUD is often supplemented by up to three multi-function displays (MFD), ie, TV tubes that can show several different types of data according to the phase of flight. One innovation is to

McDonnell Douglas' proposed 'Big Picture' will combine all the displays on a single video screen. Instead of knobs, switches and dials, this system will be activated by the pilot's touch, voice or helmet movement. (McDonnell Douglas Corp)

add immediately below the HUD another TV-type display showing (for example) the picture produced by a missile sensor, focussed at infinity. For the longer term, however, the emphasis is on replacing the separate MFDs with a single large screen, giving the pilot a more easily assimilated picture of the complete tactical situation.

Pilot workload may be reduced by the use of interactive voice systems (IVS), in which the pilot may select radio frequencies and weapons (and certain system functions) by simply asking for them, and he is provided with various types of information, especially warnings, by recorded or synthesized voices. In order to make direct voice inputs (DVI), the pilot will insert into the system his individual pre-recorded tape cassette, so that the IVS can recognise his instructions. On the subject of audible information, it is anticipated that stereo headphones will be used to permit threat warnings or a wingman's voice to seem to come from the direction in which the source lies. Other innovations made possible by advances in avionics include the monitoring of the pilot's mental state.

Sensors and Weapons

As indicated earlier, increasing emphasis will be placed on passive sensors such as IR, rather than relying on active radars that disclose the position of the transmitter. In view of the importance of beyond-visual-range (BVR) missiles, it will be vital to identify potential targets correctly, although conventional IFF (identification, friend or foe) equipment has in the past proved unreliable.

It is anticipated that radars will provide some capability in non-co-operative target recognition (NCTR), although radar may need to be supplemented by other means. Reports indicate that the USAF F-15 flies with an Eagle Eye sniper-scope fastened to the HUD for long-range target identification. Northrop TV systems have been fitted to the F-14 and F-4E for the same purpose, and GEC Avionics is developing a visual augmentation system (VAS) for the Tornado ADV.

The latest air-air missiles use multi-stage guidance that permits them to lock on to the target after launch, and allows their full aerodynamic range to be exploited. For low-drag installations they may in future be wingless, with thrust vectoring to eliminate the need for tail-fins, and thus suit internal carriage.

Automatic weapons will continue to be used, perhaps with caseless ammunition, and possibly with guided projectiles for the heavier calibres. A radar-directed trainable gun with 2 to 3 degrees of movement would give more firing opportunities and a better hit probability. Laser weapons currently appear unlikely to find application in fighters, due to the heavy weight of such armament, and atmospheric attenuation at low altitudes.

Advanced Projects

Having outlined the principal technologies that are expected to be employed in the fighters that will enter service during the 1990s, it may be

The value of a TV camera in long-range target recognition is illustrated by this image of an F-14, produced by another F-14's television camera set (TCS) at 10 times the range of the unaided eye. (Northrop Corp)

worthwhile recapping on the various technology demonstrators that are providing the foundations, before summarizing present-day knowledge on the plans for production programmes.

The **Rockwell HiMAT** unmanned research vehicle was intended specifically to explore new technologies relevant to enhanced transonic manoeuvrability. It has an arrowhead wing with a close-coupled canard, both of the surfaces featuring aeroelastic tailoring, so that they deform into an optimized shape under the design manoeuvre conditions. Some 26 per cent of the airframe is made of graphite (carbon) composites, and the metallic parts use SPF and DB, as discussed earlier.

The HiMAT vehicle weighs 3400 lb (1540 kg) when dropped from its B-52 launch aircraft, and it is powered by a single afterburning J85-GE-21 of 5000 lb (2270 kg) static thrust. The first of the two RPVs had its maiden flight on 27 July 1979, the second following two years later. With the CG set at 5 per cent of mean chord aft of low-speed aerodynamic centre (AC), HiMAT has demonstrated an 8G sustained turn at Mach 0.9 at 25,000 ft (7600 m). With the CG set on the low-speed AC (ie with neutral subsonic stability), it has also demonstrated a 4G sustained turn at Mach 1.4 at 40,000 ft (12,200 m).

The **General Dynamics AFTI/F-16** is effectively the standard fighter with modifications to permit the exploration of new ways to fly and to attack ground and air targets, and to allow testing of new cockpit concepts. Externally, the principal change is the introduction of two canard surfaces on the intake, at 15 degrees to the vertical. Internally, the aircraft has triplex digital FBW, a wide-angle HUD and two MFDs, a helmet-mounted sight, and provisions for voice control.

The flying control system provides for new modes, such as flat turns, and for the aircraft to be flown directly either by the nose radar (in air-air gunnery) or by IR/laser trackers mounted in the leading edge (for ground attack). Strikes against ground targets can be carried out automatically, once the pilot has designated the target via the HUD, using an automatic manoeuvring attack system (AMAS). The aircraft is also being used to test computer-controlled pull-ups in dive attacks as a safeguard against the pilot losing orientation or consciousness. The AFTI/F-16 first flew on 10 July 1982.

The mission-adaptive wing (MAW) concept of an aerofoil that can be cambered smoothly and automatically to suit any speed and manoeuvre combination in the aircraft's envelope is being tested in the **Boeing AFTI/F-111.** This type was chosen because its variable-sweep wing and supersonic capability allow the performance potential of the MAW to be assessed over a wide range of speeds and sweep angles, simulating different types of military aircraft.

The leading edge of the AFTI/F-111 wing bends as a single piece, but the trailing edge functions as three segments on each side, the outer two of which can act differentially for roll control. For flexibility the bending wing surfaces are made of fibreglass, a technique previously used by Boeing on the leading edge of the 747.

Seen in close formation with a standard F-16, the AFTI/F-16 is readily distinguished by its two canard surfaces, which make possible direct side-force and direct lift control. (General Dynamics)

One of the most interesting
proposals of recent years, the
McDonnell Douglas
Vectored-Lift Fighter was to
have produced direct
side-force control by means of
its vertical tails and canard,
and direct lift control by the
combined action of its
variable-incidence outer wings
and beaver-tail elevator.
(McDonnell Douglas Corp)

The Boeing AFTI/F-111 allows the mission-adaptive wing to be tested over a wide range of sweep angles and at both subsonic and supersonic speeds. (Boeing Military Airplane Co)

The AFTI/F-111 first flew on 18 October 1985. It is anticipated that the MAW will improve supersonic buffet-free lift by almost 70 per cent, and sustained lift by 25 per cent. It is also expected to reduce supersonic cruise drag by 7 per cent, and subsonic cruise drag by 6 per cent. The trailing edge deflection rate of 30 degrees per second will also give a very fast G-build-up.

A two-seat F-15B has been in use as the basis for the Integrated Flight-Fire Control **(IFFC)/Firefly III** programme, using an advanced digital flight control system, the Hughes APG-63 radar, and Martin-Marietta Atlis II pod, giving TV target acquisition and auto-track, plus laser designation and rangefinding. The General Electric Firefly III system is designed to make possible air-air gunnery in high angle-off situations and head-on, long range. It also allows air-ground ordnance to be delivered in a level high-G turn, without overflying the target.

The idea of vectoring the thrust of aft-mounted engines (as distinct from that of the centrally-mounted Pegasus in the V/STOL Harrier) is to be tested initially by placing movable vanes in the jets of an F-14 and F/A-18. A more sophisticated system is to be tested in the STOL and Manoeuvre Technology Demonstrator F-15B, or STOL Eagle, which is to fly in March 1988.

The **STOL/MTD** is to have 2-D nozzles developed by Pratt & Whitney, giving 20 degrees of vectoring on each side of the conventional thrust line, and 135 degrees of jet reversal. In bench-tests these nozzles have demonstrated the ability to produce a thrust component of 8000 lb (3630 kg) at right angles to the powerplant centreline. The aircraft is also to have an integrated flight and propulsion control (IFPC) system to ensure the safe use of thrust vectoring, and active canard surfaces on each side of the inlets. The aim is to take off with full internal fuel and a 6000 lb (2720 kg) load in a distance of 1000 ft (300 m), and land in 1250 ft (380 m) on a wet runway, allowing for cross winds gusting to 30 knots (55.6 km/hr), a cloud ceiling of 200 ft (60 m) and visibility of only 0.5 nm (925 m). To make possible precision touchdowns under these conditions without external aids, the aircraft will be equipped with the Hughes APG-70 high-resolution radar from the F-15E.

Turning from demonstrators that are intended to investigate literally one or two new technologies to brand-new aircraft that are designed virtually as prototypes for the new generation, Europe now has two such aircraft in the form of the Dassault-Breguet Rafale-A and the **British Aerospace EAP** (Experimental Aircraft Programme).

The EAP was produced largely on a national basis, funded jointly by the British Government and industry, because of concern in the UK over the time taken to launch the four-nation EFA (European Fighter Aircraft). Although it was impossible to make the EAP entirely representative of the EFA (the shape and equipment of which was still under discussion at the time), EAP was to provide invaluable information on the technologies that were to be employed. These included an unstable close-coupled canard-delta configuration, full-authority digital FBW controls, the use of

composite materials and new alloys, an electronic cockpit, a variable geometry chin intake, low-drag weapons carriage and digital databus avionics.

The EAP demonstrator has an empty weight of approximately 22,000 lb (9977 kg) and a wing area of 560 sq ft (52 m²). It is powered by two Turbo-Union RB.199 Mk104D turbofans, each providing around 17,000 lb (7700 kg) of afterburning thrust. It has a cranked delta wing with a rounded tip and a straight trailing edge, and a small leading edge root extension over the chin intake. The intakes are two-dimensional and designed to function efficiently to an AOA of at least 30 degrees, using a hinged lower lip or 'vari-cowl'.

Taking off for the first time, the British Aerospace EAP shows its leading edge flaps and vari-cowl intakes. (British Aerospace)

The wing is set low on the basic fuselage shape, although the intakes project below it, producing a deep side-view. The foreplane is set well forward to improve the pilot's rear view, though obviously at some cost in view forward and downward. The EAP has the vertical tail of the Tornado, but with a rounded tip for aesthetic reasons. It has quadruplex digital FBW controls with no electrical or mechanical reversion. This system operates 15 surfaces: the two foreplanes, four leading edge flaps, four flaperons, two inlet cowls, two airbrakes and the rudder. Longitudinal control uses a combination of foreplanes and flaperons. Roll control makes use of all four flaperons at low speed, but at high speeds only the inboard pair is used. The EAP first flew on 8 August 1986.

Although a reasonably elegant design, the EAP has a very deep fuselage due to its chin intakes, and a large (Tornado-type) vertical tail for natural directional stability. (British Aerospace)

The production aircraft for which the EAP is laying the groundwork is the **Eurofighter EFA,** an 800 aircraft programme combining the requirements and the industries of Britain, West Germany, Italy and Spain. The programme is to be managed by a company known as Eurofighter/Jagdflugzeug GmbH, formed for this project by the four partner companies, ie, Aeritalia (AIT), BAe, Germany's MBB, and Spain's CASA. Britain and Germany will each have a 33 per cent share, Italy 21 per cent and Spain 13 per cent. The new EJ200 engines, with a production run of around 2,000 units, will be developed and manufactured by a new joint engine company, Eurojet Engines GmbH, combining the interests of Rolls-Royce, Germany's MTU, Fiat Aviazione, and SENER of Spain.

The Eurofighter will be marginally smaller than the EAP, with an empty weight of 21,500 lb (9750 kg), and a wing area of 538 sq ft (50 m²). Its Eurojet EJ200 engines will each provide an afterburning thrust of around 20,000 lb (9070 kg). They will have a thrust/weight ratio of 10:1, a pressure ratio of more than 25:1, and a bypass ratio of approximately 0.4.

This new aircraft will also differ from the EAP in having a straight leading edge, missiles on the wingtips (rather than underneath), and a smaller fin, the aircraft being designed to be naturally unstable directionally. It will also have a new

An artist's impression of what
the four-nation Eurofighter
EFA is expected to look like.
In comparison with the EAP,
note the straight leading edge,
wingtip fairings, and much
smaller fin.
(Eurofighter/Jagdflugzeug)

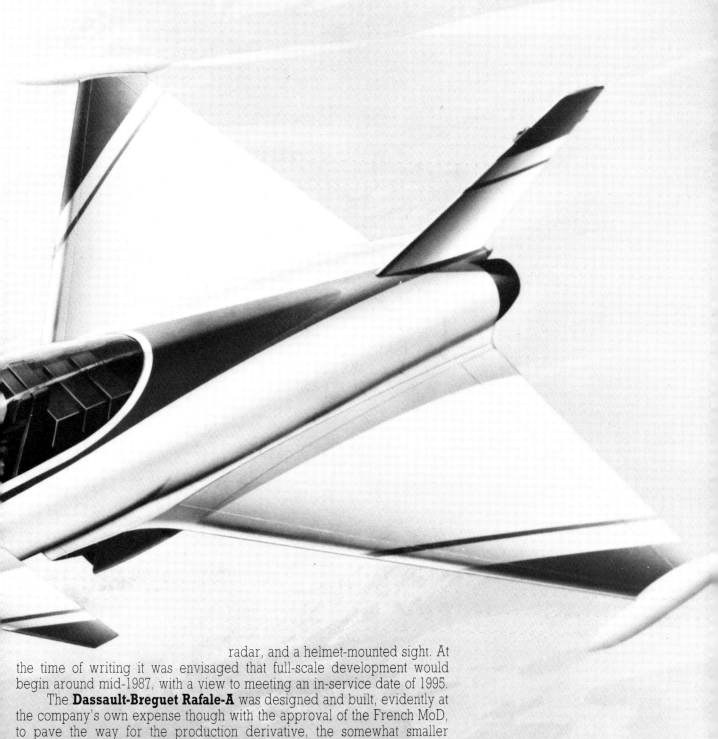

radar, and a helmet-mounted sight. At
the time of writing it was envisaged that full-scale development would
begin around mid-1987, with a view to meeting an in-service date of 1995.
  The **Dassault-Breguet Rafale-A** was designed and built, evidently at
the company's own expense though with the approval of the French MoD,
to pave the way for the production derivative, the somewhat smaller

Rafale-B. The technology demonstrator first flew on 4 July 1986, and is marginally lighter than Britain's EAP, which had its maiden flight a month later.

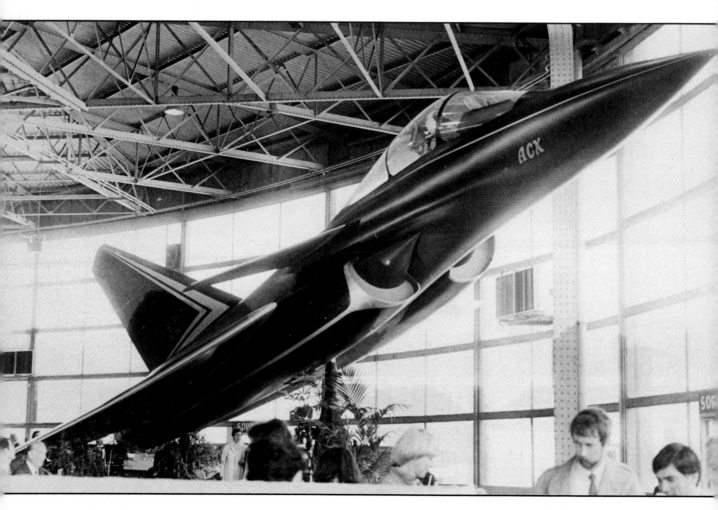

The Rafale-A has an empty weight of approximately 21,000 lb (9500 kg) and a wing area of 506 sq ft (47 m²). It is powered by two General Electric F404 engines of 17,200 lb (7800 kg) thrust. Like the EAP, it has a modified delta wing with a cranked leading edge, but the Rafale has slight forward sweep on the trailing edge and square-cut tips to carry missile rails.

The wing is mid-set on the fuselage, and the foreplane is located behind the cockpit. The intakes are placed in what might be termed 'grooves' in the lower fuselage sides, which provides much better separation (eliminating the possibility of one engine surge affecting the other side) and more scope for centreline stores. This intake location is highly innovative, though it currently remains to be seen whether it can cope with large AOAs. Like the EAP, the Rafale-A has approximately 25

As originally proposed, the Dassault-Breguet ACX, which later became the Rafale (Gust), was to have had multi-shock conical intakes. The ACX mockup was shown at the Paris Salon in June 1983. (Roy Braybrook)

per cent of its structure made in carbon composites.

The production **Rafale-B** is to be an even lighter aircraft, with an empty weight of around 18,750 lb (8500 kg) and a wing area of 473.4 sq ft (44 m²). The composite content of the airframe is expected to rise to around 35 per cent. It will be powered by two SNECMA M88 engines of 18,750 lb (8500 kg) thrust each. The M88 will have a bypass ratio of around 0.5, and a pressure ratio of over 24:1.

The Rafale-A technology demonstrator lacks the shock-cones of the ACX, but it has large splitter plates to prevent ingestion of the fuselage boundary layer. (AMD-BA)

Six prototypes of the Rafale-B are to be constructed, including two naval aircraft and one two-seater. All the prototypes will fly in 1990-91, and production deliveries will begin in late 1995 or early 1996. The domestic market is for 250 of the land-based version, and 85 of the naval version. In addition, it seems likely that France will win support from some of the European nations involved in the F-16 programme, such as Belgium, and possibly Denmark, the Netherlands and Norway. Dassault-Breguet estimates the potential market at 1000 Rafale-Bs.

At the time of writing the future of the **Israel Aircraft Industries Lavi** project is in doubt, due to the need for US financial support for what amounts to a competitor for the F-16. If it goes ahead, the Lavi will replace the A-4 and Kfir in Israeli service, providing a domestic market for 300 units. The Lavi is a much smaller aircraft than either the Eurofighter EFA or the Rafale-B, being designed around a single Pratt & Whitney PW1120 engine of 20,260 lbs (9200 kg) afterburning thrust. It has a wing area of 360 sq ft (33.5 m²), a basic take-off weight of 22,000 lb (10,000 kg) and a maximum take-off weight of 37,500 lb (17,000 kg).

Designed to fulfil the interdiction and close support roles, the Lavi is of canard configuration with a cropped arrowhead wing planform and a

Probably the best-looking fighter to emerge in the 1980s, the Rafale-A is laying the groundwork for the somewhat smaller Rafale-B, which will be produced in both land-based and carrier-based versions. (AMD-BA)

close-coupled foreplane. The early three-view drawings indicated it would have a chin intake with a horizontal ramp (a surprising feature for a ground attack aeroplane) and a single vertical tail, although two retractable ventral fins were added later. Around 22 per cent of the airframe is to be composite construction. Following first flight on 31 December 1986, it was planned to begin deliveries in 1990 with a view to IOC in 1992.

The first prototype of the Israel Aircraft Industries Lavi (Young Lion) is a two-seater. Note the canard, wing-body blending, tall fin, and retractable ventral fins. (IAI)

The smallest of the new fighter generation is Sweden's **JAS 39 Gripen** (Griffon), which is designed to fulfil the fighter, attack and reconnaissance roles. That it is much smaller than the preceding Viggen appears to be explained mainly by the fact that the JAS 39 will use guided weapons against all types of targets, with no requirement for 'iron bombs'. It is to be powered by the RM12 Volvo Flygmotor derivative of the F404 engine, giving a thrust of 18,000 lb (8165 kg). Basic take-off weight is also 18,000 lb.

The configuration adopted for the JAS 39 is a cropped delta with leading edge sawtooth and a close-coupled foreplane set behind the cockpit. One unusual feature is the use of lateral intakes, which are generally considered unsuitable for operation at a high AOA.

The first of five JAS 39 prototypes is due to fly in 1987, leading to service entry in 1992. The development contract included an initial production batch of 30 aircraft, with options on a further 110, although the domestic market in replacing Viggens and Drakens could easily run to more than 300 units.

Sweden's JAS 39 Gripen (Griffon), shown here in mock-up form, is unusual in having lateral intakes, which are widely regarded as unsuitable for operation at high angles of attack. (A. Andersson, Saab-Scania)

The most futuristic fighter currently planned in the West is the USAF's **Advanced Tactical Fighter** (ATF), which is scheduled to replace the F-15, the potential domestic market being at least 750 aircraft. The ATF will combine a wide range of new technologies in order to provide sustained supersonic combat capability, STOL performance, stealth characteristics, and reduced maintenance demands. It is expected to have up to 50 per cent of its structure built in advanced composites, the latest avionics systems, and two new engines, the P&W YF119 or GE YF120. Each engine will produce over 30,000 lb (13,600 kg) in static thrust.

The first major step in the ATF programme was the selection of contractor-teams in October 1986, each to produce two prototypes. Lockheed is prime contractor for the YF-22A, with Boeing and General Dynamics as principal subcontractors, while Northrop is prime contractor on the YF-23A, with McDonnell Douglas as principal sub-contractor. One prototype of each design will have the P&W engine and the other the GE engine. Normal gross weight is expected to be approximately 50,000 lb (22,700 kg). Flight testing is to begin in late 1989 in order to begin production deliveries in 1994.

The ATF will make much greater use of stealth technology than the smaller European fighters. Little has been made public of the demonstrator aircraft that have proved the feasibility of achieving low signatures, but it is known that in 1976 Lockheed was funded to produce five XSTs (experimental stealth technology) vehicles. The first XST flew in November

Some clues to the form of the YF-23A may have been provided by this model of an 'Advanced Medium Fighter' shown by Northrop at the Hanover Air Show in June 1986. (Northrop Corp)

1977 and was described as being of 'bat-like appearance'. It was a small aircraft powered by two non-afterburning General Electric J85 turbojets of around 3500 lb (1600 kg) thrust.

The XST was evidently successful, as Lockheed was in 1981 awarded a contract to develop a full-scale single-seat 'covert survivable in-weather reconnaissance and strike' (CSIRS) fighter, the F-19A. Reports suggest that 20 F-19As were purchased initially, but that later orders covered a further 100 units. The F-19A is powered by two non-afterburning GE F404 engines, giving around 11,000 lb (5000 kg) thrust. It first flew in 1982, and is believed to be taken to its operating bases inside the hold of a C-5A transport. Aside from its diminutive size and low temperature jets, the F-19A is believed to owe its small signature to the use of composite materials, radar-absorbent paint, sound-absorbing panels in the intake ducts and jetpipes, engine silencers developed by Rohr Industries, adaptive camouflage, and the use of only passive sensors.

Looking further into the future, the US is investigating the possibility of developing a hypersonic interceptor that would protect the continental US and naval battle groups against attack by high speed bombers and cruise missiles. Designated LORAINE (LOng RAnge INterceptor Experiment), this vehicle would cruise at perhaps Mach 10. Significantly, LORAINE is envisaged as an unmanned vehicle, indicating that within the forseeable future the time will come for black boxes to take over completely from the human pilot, at least in the air-air role.

Opposite left: A Lockheed artist's conception of the ATF, designed to combine low observable technology, protracted supersonic cruise, and STOL performance. (Lockheed Corp)

List of Abbreviations

AC	aerodynamic centre
ACF	Air Combat Fighter (USAF)
ADC	Aerospace Defense Command (USAF)
ADV	Air Defence Variant (Tornado)
AFTI	Advanced Fighter Technologies Integration
AI	air intercept (radar)
AIT	Aeritalia
AMAS	Automated Maneuvering Attack System
AMRAAM	Advanced Medium-Range Air-Air Missile
AOA	angle of attack
ASAT	anti-satellite
ASPJ	Airborne Self-Protection Jammer
ASRAAM	Advanced Short-Range Air-Air Missile
ATE	Advanced Technology Engine
BAe	British Aerospace
BVR	beyond visual range (missile)
CAF	Canadian Armed Forces
CAP	combat air patrol
CG	centre of gravity
D	dimensional (as in 2-D)
D	drag

DB	diffusion bonding
DLC	direct lift control
DSFC	direct side-force control
DVI	direct voice-input
EAP	Experimental Aircraft Programme (BAe/MoD)
ECCM	electronic counter-countermeasures
ECM	electronic countermeasures
ECR	Electronic Combat and Reconnaissance (Tornado)
EFA	European Fighter Aircraft (Eurofighter)
F	fighter
FBW	fly-by-wire (electrically-signalled controls)
FLIR	Forward-Looking IR
FSW	forward-swept wing
GE	General Electric
GmbH	*Gesellschaft mit beschraenkter Haftung* (a German limited liability company)
GPS	Global Positioning System
HiMAT	Highly Maneuverable Aircraft Technology
HMS	helmet-mounted sight
HOTAS	hands-on-throttle-and-stick
HUD	head-up display
IAS	indicated airspeed
IDS	Interdiction/Strike (Tornado)
IFF	identification, friend or foe
IFFC	integrated fire and flight controls
IIAF	Imperial Iranian Air Force
IIR	imaging infra-red
IOC	initial operational capability
IVS	interactive voice system
L	lift
LANTIRN	Low Altitude Navigation and Targeting IR for Night
L/D	lift/drag ratio
LEX	leading edge extension
LORAINE	LOng RAnge INterceptor Experiment
LWF	LightWeight Fighter
MAW	mission-adaptive wing
MBB	Messerschitt-Boelkow-Blohm
MFD	multi-function display
MiG	Mikoyan-Gurevich
MoD	Ministry of Defence

MTD	Maneuver Technology Demonstrator
MTU	Motoren- und Turbinen-Union
MW	*Mehrzweckwaffe* (multi-purpose weapon)
NASA	National Aeronautics and Space Administration
NASARR	North American Search and Ranging Radar
NCTI/R	non-co-operative target identification/recognition
OCU	operational capabilities upgrade (in RAF use, OCU signifies Operational Conversion Unit)
P&W	Pratt & Whitney
RAAF	Royal Australian Air Force
RAF	Royal Air Force
RAM	radar-absorbent material
RCS	radar cross-section
RFP	request for proposals
RPV	remotely-piloted vehicle
RSS	relaxed static stability
RWR	radar-warning receiver
SAC	Strategic Air Command (USAF)
SEP	specific excess power
SFC	specific fuel consumption
SMTD	Stol and Maneuver Technology Demonstrator
SPF	superplastic forming
STOL	short take-off and landing
Su	Sukhoi
T	thrust
TAC	Tactical Air Command (USAF)
t/c	thickness/chord ratio
Tu	Tupolev
T/W	thrust/weight ratio
USAF	United States Air Force
USN	United States Navy
V	velocity
VAS	Visual Augmentation System (GEC Avionics)
V/STOL	vertical or short take-off and landing
W	weight
WW	World War
Yak	Yakovlev

Index